# CLIMBING TOWARD THE LIGHT

## HOPE FOR THOSE SUFFERING FROM DEPRESSION

By Mark Litzsinger
with Sarah Hamaker

**Climbing Toward the Light: Hope for Those Suffering From Depression**
By Mark Litzsinger
with Sarah Hamaker

ISBN: 978-0-9980204-3-3

Cover and interior design by Collin Smith.

Printed in the United States of America.

*This book is dedicated to Bonnie Senner, Dr. Bill Scheftner, Dick and Dona Litzsinger, and my siblings, Robin, Heidi, Shawn, and Todd. Without your encouragement, support, listening skills, patience, and medical knowledge, I would probably not be here today. And I would not have been able to write this book with the help of the wonderful Sarah Hamaker and her skilled support staff, including Connor Stratman and researcher Whitney Hopler.*

*No one gets through life for free and without hardship—there are many bumps on the road along the way. We all face challenges, regardless of our economic standing. Dedication and perseverance are the keys to overcoming these obstacles and each hurdle conquered makes us stronger and better capable of handling the next hurdle.*

# TABLE OF CONTENTS

# FOREWARD

The state of the mental health of Americans may surprise and shock you. In any given year, 43.8 million adults experience some form of mental illness. By diagnosis, approximately 1 percent of the population lives with schizophrenia, 2.6 percent with bipolar disorder, 6.9 percent with major depression (Mark's disease), and 18 percent with anxiety disorders. One in five children between the ages of 13 and 18 has, or will have, a serious mental illness. Suicide is the second leading cause of death in young people between the ages of 15 and 24, and 90 percent of those had an underlying mental illness.

Considering these statistics, you might wonder why there isn't more dialogue to gain understanding and to ensure adequate treatment and support for families and persons living with a mental illness. The bottom line is that mental illness is still seen as a stigma. This stigma is rooted in our history when it was an embarrassment for families to have a member with mental illness. Many considered mental illness or addiction a moral failure instead of an illness. It is time we move beyond these outmoded conceptions and become educated.

Stigma stifles communication, isolating the person with a mental illness as well as his or her family members. It prevents others from understanding and helping. Stories are an excellent way to reduce stigma. Intellectual descriptions of mental illness help somewhat, but I think stories are the best vehicle for learning about this subject, especially when the stories are from someone who has personal experience. When you hear such personal stories about mental illness, then it becomes clear that each person's journey is different and that he or she remains a unique human being.

Mark's very personal story about his own battle with depression helps us understand why we need books like this. He describes his brothers, sisters, and others worrying about his erratic behavior. His parents struggled with understanding what was going on during his periods of severe depression. As chairman of a billion-dollar company, he had nowhere to hide.

When I read the first edition of this book, there were times I almost asked aloud, "Where were those who could educate the family on the disease?" A person's support system, family, friends, and work colleagues can't help if they don't know what is going on. For Mark, how scary this period must have been, wondering what was happening to him and why he couldn't live up to his expectations for himself. By sharing his experiences in this book, Mark is helping others to become more aware of the disease, symptoms, treatments, and the need for support for both the person living with a mental illness, and those caring for that person.

I have my own personal journey. My wife and I were once helpless parents trying to do our best for a child with mental illness. That led us to the National Alliance on Mental Illness (NAMI), a national organization with state and local chapters dedicated to education, advocacy, and support for families and persons living with a mental illness. A signature program of NAMI is "Family to Family," a 12-week class taught by peers for caregivers. This class is designed to enable them to take the leadership role with their loved one in understanding the disease, ensuring support mechanisms are in place, and advocating for their care. What a shame this program did not come to the attention of Mark's family.

Our society needs to get more comfortable talking about mental illness, its symptoms, treatments, and needed support. Sensational news accounts of bizarre or dangerous behavior of someone with a mental illness need to be balanced by stories of people struggling with the disease while still trying to be productive persons. Mark accomplished this in writing his book.

We need to educate our legislators so they realize mental illness is just another illness, one of the brain. Medical care needs to be available to those with mental illness, something that for too long had only limited coverage in health-insurance policies. As a result of insurance restrictions and lack of government programs, the current support network for mental illness is weak. Mark had the benefit of being able to afford the best treatment available, but not everyone is so lucky.

But there is hope. The National Institute of Mental Health is funding research in new and exciting directions. The ability to see results through brain scans helps accelerate understanding. Data-driven research is opening many new avenues. We hope that we can move beyond treating symptoms to finding some cures. However, we should not minimize the importance of treating symptoms to enable someone to lead a more normal life. Thankfully, there is now a much more active dialogue on mental illness, which will hopefully lead to greater understanding and support.

John Schladweiler
Board President
NAMI Illinois
August 2017

"Life is made of choices, some good and some not so good. As we make choices, hopefully we learn from our experiences, which make us stronger and more resilient. As we grow older, our choices help us navigate through the high waves and winds we experience here on Earth. The lesson learned is to choose wisely with due diligence and forethought."

—Mark Litzsinger

"There is no normal life that is free of pain. It's that very wrestling with our problems that can be the impetus for our growth."

—Fred Rogers, American television host

# INTRODUCTION

**"But with the slow menace of a glacier, depression came on. No one had any measure of its progress; no one had any plan for stopping it. Everyone tried to get out of its way."**
—Frances Perkins, U.S. Secretary of Labor from 1933 to 1945

Imagine a fog that permeates every aspect of your life. It clouds your thinking. It muddles your brain. It makes it difficult to refocus your attention. It's like you're living as a ghost, watching the real world from afar. That's how some have described what it's like to live with depression.

Others talk about depression as a dark place, a fall into a bottomless shaft, drowning, and having no joy. Sometimes depression is described as nothingness, torture, or a cancer of the soul. Still others say depression makes them feel like they're in a whirlpool, a constant circle with no exit.

That's an apt description for how I felt when depressed. For me, depression was a continuous circle, an ever-deepening gulf that sucked me down for months at a time. All I ever wanted was to be a normal person with a good job and career. Then depression hit me again and again and again, taking years of my life.

My story isn't unique—those who suffer from depression will recognize glimpses of themselves in my trajectory. But by sharing my experience, I hope to encourage others to seek help. I also hope to provide guidance for families and friends fighting alongside those with depression, helping them to get to a healthier place. This is my story and I hope it will help others looking for hope and help.

I first encountered depression as I was about to embark on my adult life after college. Up to that point in my life, I had had many successes, including playing on two state championship tennis teams at Hinsdale Central High School in Hinsdale, Illinois. I had many friends—and girlfriends—throughout high school and college, and was the president of the Phi Kappa Sigma fraternity while at Texas Christian University in Fort Worth, Texas.

As the oldest of five children and the eldest grandchild, I was expected to set a good example for my siblings and cousins. For the most part, I lived up to my family's expectations—that doesn't mean my friends and I didn't occasionally party on the weekends and drink, which we did, but overall I stayed on the straight and narrow path.

When I went off to Texas Christian University in 1974, I played tennis for the university and joined the Phi Kappa Sigma fraternity. I went to class, got good grades, played tennis, and partied with my frat brothers, and still managed to graduate in four years—no problem.

After graduation, I wasn't sure what career I wanted to pursue, so when there was a chance to work at my family's company, the Follett Corporation, I took it. I started my career there in the College Bookstore Division (Follett College Stores). The 145-year-old company, headquartered in Westchester, Illinois, is a lease operator of college bookstores—among other businesses—in the educational marketplace. The Follett Corporation is a $3.6 billion company started in 1873, before being taken over by my great-grandfather, C.W. Follett, in the early years of the twentieth century.

My first position in the college bookstore division was as a management trainee at the bookstore at Saddleback Community College in Mission Viejo, California. I was lucky enough to choose where I would do my training. I wanted to go to California because of the good-looking women in their bikinis, the music, and the laid-back lifestyle—you can tell my priorities in starting a new job were slightly off. I was able to afford a nice apartment and a car on a starting salary of $8,000 per year.

I had been in California for approximately three months when one morning I woke up in my bed and stared at the ceiling instead of getting up right away. I knew something was wrong. I felt down and lonely. I signed up for a class at the college so that I could see the college psychologist to see what was going on. After a few sessions—including one in which he tried to hypnotize me—I could tell that seeing this particular doctor wasn't working.

The only relative living near me in California was my grandmother, who resided in West Lake Village. I visited her and told her how I was feeling. She was comforting and supportive, but despite her efforts, I continue on a downward spiral. Finally, after six months, I talked to the Follett-run regional manager of the bookstore division about transferring back to the Illinois area to be closer to home, thinking that I might just be homesick. He transferred me to the off-campus bookstore at the University of Illinois in Champaign, Illinois.

I became one of the assistant managers of the store while still in training. Within a two- to three-month period, my depression seemed to go away. I now know this is called "cycling out." I was happy again and learned a lot at the store over the next two years. Then things began to unravel and this time it wasn't an easy climb back to "normal."

Many people don't know they have depression after their first episode. Like me, you might think that you just aren't feeling well. Perhaps you hope these emotions will pass and you'll get back to the status quo on your own. That didn't happen for me after the first initial episode. When I experienced other bouts with depression, I needed professional help to recover. The assistance of several doctors and therapists, working alongside me, provided the means to get me on the road to recovery.

What I'm trying to do within these pages is offer patients, potential patients, families, friends, and doctors encouragement and education about depression. This is a disease that doctors still don't completely understand. This is a disease that some who suffer from it still don't want to talk about it with their families or doctors. This is a disease that doesn't always completely go away. This is a disease that can take years to come to a place of wellness.

"The public's view of depression is really influenced by several things," says Dr. William Scheftner, psychopharmacologist and former chairman of the Department of Psychiatry at Rush University Medical Center in Chicago, Illinois.[1] "First, depression tends to be a recurrent and sometimes chronic illness. No matter how well intentioned one is, if you're living with someone who every two years feels awful and can't function to pull his share of the load, it becomes difficult to be accepting of this as an illness."

## Coronavirus Pandemic's Impact

As I update this introduction in the spring of 2021, I grieve with my fellow Americans over the past year. We have learned many hard lessons through the COVID-19 lockdowns and the burning of our cities during the riots of 2020. We've lost loved ones to COVID-19, both to the disease itself and through the mental-health issues the virus exacerbated. As a country—indeed as the world—we are all hurting.

As you'll read in this updated edition, the coronavirus pandemic has upended our way of life and triggered depressive episodes in many people, both young and old, rich and poor, in cities and in rural areas. We are facing one of the greatest health crisis in living history, one that has tested our strength, our resilience, and our national identity.

But I encourage you to be strong in protecting your loved ones and friends. We are Americans with a history of bravery when faced with adversity. The Unites States is the envy of the world when we are strong and united, and pursue our dreams under the guidance and wisdom of our Founding Fathers. We are the land of the free and home of the brave. Be strong and resilient. We are Americans—strong and dedicated—and we will overcome COVID-19 like we have other adversaries.

In this new edition, we've addressed how the coronavirus pandemic impacts mental health. One thing the coronavirus pandemic has taught us is that we are not isolated here in America—we are part of a wide world. Our struggles here mirror the struggles in Africa, in Europe, in Asia, in Australia. COVID-19 impacted the far corners of the world, and we all bore each other's sufferings as one people. To help broaden our understanding, we've included a new chapter on depression across the globe. We've also explored the relationship of depression and loneliness, depression and addiction, and depression and technology.

Finally, wherever you are on this journey with depression—whether you're the patient, a family member, part of the medical profession, or ancillary services—increasing your knowledge and understanding of how depression impacts patients and family members, how the past has shaped current treatment methods, and what the future holds for those who suffer from this disease will provide a firm foundation from which to go forward. The goal of this book is to do just that—to give patients, family members, doctors, and others who wish to learn more a blueprint of the disease's history and treatments, as well as offer hope for a future in recovery.

PART I: THE DISEASE

# CHAPTER ONE
## A BRIEF HISTORY OF DEPRESSION

**"That's the thing about depression: A human being can survive almost anything, as long as she sees the end in sight. But depression is so insidious, and it compounds daily, that it's impossible to ever see the end. The fog is like a cage without a key."**
—Elizabeth Wurtzel, American author of *Prozac Nation*

Like most diseases of the mind, depression has been misunderstood, mislabeled, and misdiagnosed throughout the ages. Before we can delve into what we know about depression today, we need to take a brief look back at how depression has been viewed and treated in the past.

Although people have suffered from depression throughout recorded history, our opinion of the disease has changed dramatically over the years. We've come a long way in our understanding about what may cause depression and how best to treat it. "The story of depression is one in which we seem to witness a comparatively consistent disease phenomenon that is nevertheless endlessly [reconceptualized] and lived according to the experience of the particular culture and individual concerned."[2]

From the ancient world's "melancholia" to the Enlightenment's more natural view of depression on to the twentieth century's more scientific viewpoint, depression has evolved from a state of mind to a disease with genetic traits. Let's examine the changes throughout the years in how the medical profession handled depression.

## Melancholia

Documented reports of people afflicted by this disease go back to ancient Mesopotamia. Texts from this early human civilization describe people suffering from symptoms that match what we currently call depression, but which has been called different names—one being "melancholia"—in different time periods.

From the first reports about the disease when human writing first developed (between 1,000 and 2,000 B.C.) until the end of the Middle Ages in the 1400s A.D., the predominant view on depression was that it was caused by evil spirits (demons) who were possessing the souls of depressed people. However, Hippocrates, the ancient Greek physician, dissented from this view with his belief that all illnesses were caused by imbalanced bodily fluids. According to Hippocrates, depression resulted from people having too much black bile in their spleens.

Treatments for depression from ancient times through the Middle Ages varied widely. The treatments—designed to banish evil spirits and to prevent evil from spreading and infecting others—included:

- exorcism
- torture
- burning
- drowning

In ancient times, people suffering from depression often felt religious guilt because of their illness, fearing that their own sin was to blame for causing the disease and that if they could only try hard enough to avoid sin, they would get better. They felt shame, as well, when other believers assumed that God was punishing them through their disease.

Those in agreement with Hippocrates' belief that depression had a physical cause suggested less-extreme treatments for the disease, such as:

- bloodletting
- diet changes
- herbal remedies
- exercise
- bathing

**A More Enlightened View**

During the Renaissance, from the fourteenth to the seventeenth century, the predominant view on depression was that the disease was caused by natural (rather than supernatural) factors. The previous emphasis on spiritual warfare changed to a focus on physical and mental issues. Depressed people were advised to consider how the state of their bodies and minds might be causing their depression. Physical treatments like the ones Hippocrates had suggested became more popular.

People of the Renaissance era also began to consider mental treatments after the publication in 1621 of the landmark book *The Anatomy of Melancholy* by Robert Burton, which argued that causes for depression went beyond spiritual and physical health, and could include poverty and loneliness. Burton suggested treating depressed patients via friendship, marriage, travel, and listening, which were designed to improve the overall quality of their lives.

In the Age of Enlightenment (1700s and early 1800s), many people thought that depression was caused by an inherent weakness in a person's temperament. Although depression was still treated, the purpose of treatment was no longer to cure the disease—because a cure wasn't thought to be possible—but to lessen the severity of it. This predominant view led to many depressed people being shunned as hopeless cases by society and ending up homeless or locked away in mental institutions.

The late 1800s saw the development of modern psychiatry, which revolutionized the way people thought about depression. Influential psychiatrists like Sigmund Freud theorized that depression was a result of people suffering significant losses in their lives. These doctors or psychiatrists pointed to both mental and physical factors as contributors to depression, noting that evidence of the disease could be found in depressed people's brains. In 1895, Emil Kraepelin, a German psychiatrist, officially classified depression as a disease in the new medical field of psychiatry.

"As ways of understanding the human mind and body were profoundly transformed within a modern scientific framework, 'the emotions' as an all-compassing category and process that was at once physiological and psychological—and not necessarily subject to volition—soon eclipsed its spiritual predecessors in medico-scientific literature."[3]

The current concept of depression gained ground during the late nineteenth century and "continues to evolve in the present day."[4] Once again, people began to believe that there was hope those suffering from depression could be cured. But many treatments for the disease from the late 1800s until the mid-1900s were daunting. Treatments included:

- psychiatric counseling
- electroshock
- water immersion
- lobotomy (surgically severing connections in the brain's prefrontal lobes)

### A Twentieth-Century Observation

During the 1950s, a view emerged that there were two basic types of depression and that they should be treated differently according to their different causes. Endogenous depression originated within the brain, whereas neurotic depression came from factors in depressed people's environments.

The discovery, in 1952, that a medication called isoniazid used to treat tuberculosis (TB) also was effective at treating depression led many doctors to begin prescribing medications to treat depression. "In post-World War II United States, a lot of people had TB, and it turned out that one of the anti-tubercular agents—something called MAOIs [monoamine oxidase inhibitors]—actually worked as an antidepressant as well," explains Dr. Scheftner. "As these antidepressants were developed, people began to see a connection between medication helping depressed people, which meant there had to be something physiologic or physically involved in depression."

Thus, although people suffering from depression still pursued psychiatric therapy like counseling, many also began to take medicine for their condition. A new class of drugs called "antidepressants" debuted in 1957.

"The first antidepressant to gain widespread use was imipramine, the first drug in the tricyclic antidepressant family," says Dr. Scheftner. (See Chapter 13 for more on depression treatments of the twentieth century.) "Antidepressants have resulted in moral, political, and social debates over depression. ... Yet depression goes far beyond medication. Considered by psychiatric epidemiology as the most common mental disorder since 1970, it has a vaster and more complex history than simply as an emblem of psychopharmacology. And it is at the heart of the tensions of modern individualism. This is why we need to listen less to the antidepressant and more to the spirit of depression."[5]

## The Mainstreaming of Depression

The arrival of Prozac in 1988 helped to "normalize" depression. That drug—the most widely prescribed antidepressant medication so far in history—has been touted by many in the medical profession as a simple solution for depression that tends to cause fewer side effects than other antidepressants while elevating patients' moods. The prevalence of people taking Prozac for a host of reasons, including depression, helped to remove some of the stigma of mental illness. (See Chapter 3 for more on how depression was, and is, perceived by society.)

The current views on treating depression take into account a wide array of possible contributing factors. Patients and their doctors can now choose from a host of physical, mental, emotional, and spiritual treatments to try to improve their quality of life while managing depression. These treatments include medications, psychiatric counseling, exercise, diet and sleep changes, stress reduction, and prayer.

Medical professionals are still learning what may cause depression, as well as how best to treat the disease. Depression has "ended up being the label that includes all of modern humanity's suffering. ... Depression speaks to us of illness, unhappiness, misfortune, and failure. ... We have trouble seeing clearly because depression, far from being a problem of distinguishing the normal from the pathological, brings together such a diversity of symptoms that the difficulty of defining and diagnosing it is a constant fact of psychiatry."[6]

Even as depressed people and those who seek to help them grapple with determining causes and treatments, more and more people are diagnosed with the disease. "According to The Royal College of Psychiatrists [in the United Kingdom], 'by 2020 it is estimated that depression will be the second most common disabling condition in the world,' a figure it derives from the World Health Organization. Depression is, it seems, rapidly becoming a global threat."[7]

Many times those who have depression don't even realize they're sick. I had no idea I had it when I experienced my first bout with depression as a young college graduate. I just knew I felt like crap—not necessarily from a physical standpoint but from a mental standpoint. For me, it was like losing a baseball game and having a continuous feeling of being down.

What many people don't realize is that depression may have a genetic link. "The family studies coming out indicate that people who have depression are much more likely to have family histories of depressions," notes Dr. Scheftner. "That is to say they are more likely to have a first-degree relative—a mother, father, brother, or sister—who also suffers from depression."

My own experience, which is by no means unusual, underscores the importance of depression screening. In January 2016, the U.S. Preventive Services Task Force recommended that "all American adults should be screened for depression as part of their normal health-care routine."[8] This move recognizes how common depression has become, with researchers finding an increase in the mental illness recently related to the stress and fears of modern life.

Although only a doctor can provide an accurate diagnosis, here are the eleven most common symptoms of depression, according to Bethesda, Maryland's National Institute of Mental Health:

1. Difficulty concentrating, remembering details, and making decisions.
2. Fatigue and decreased energy.
3. Feelings of guilt, worthlessness, and/or helplessness.
4. Feelings of hopelessness and/or pessimism.
5. Insomnia, early-morning wakefulness, or excessive sleeping.

6. Irritability, restlessness.
7. Loss of interest in activities or hobbies once pleasurable, including sex.
8. Overeating or appetite loss.
9. Persistent aches or pains, headaches, cramps, or digestive problems that do not ease even with treatment.
10. Persistent sad, anxious, or "empty" feelings.
11. Thoughts of suicide, suicide attempts.

If you have experienced several of these symptoms over an extended period of time, please see your primary-care physician for a depression screening. If you suspect a family member may be depressed, strongly urge the person to see a doctor immediately. What we now know about depression is that with the assistance of doctors, medications, and therapy, people with depression can recover and have happy, fulfilled lives.

## Behavioral Health Screening: What to Expect

Here is an example of the type of screening a mental-health professional might give to patients with depressive symptoms. Note that this is for informational purposes only and not for diagnostic purposes. Please consult your own medical professional to be screened for depression.

1. **Little interest in doing things.**
   ☐ NOT AT ALL   ☐ SOME DAYS
   ☐ MORE THAN HALF THE DAYS   ☐ NEARLY EVERY DAY

2. **Feeling down, depressed, or hopeless.**
   ☐ NOT AT ALL   ☐ SOME DAYS
   ☐ MORE THAN HALF THE DAYS   ☐ NEARLY EVERY DAY

3. **Poor appetite or overeating.**
   ☐ NOT AT ALL   ☐ SOME DAYS
   ☐ MORE THAN HALF THE DAYS   ☐ NEARLY EVERY DAY

4. **Feeling bad about yourself, that you're a failure, or that you've let your family down.**
   ☐ NOT AT ALL   ☐ SOME DAYS
   ☐ MORE THAN HALF THE DAYS   ☐ NEARLY EVERY DAY

5. **Thoughts that you would be better off dead or of hurting yourself.**
   ☐ NOT AT ALL   ☐ SOME DAYS
   ☐ MORE THAN HALF THE DAYS   ☐ NEARLY EVERY DAY

6. **Moving or speaking so slowly others have noticed. Or being too fidgety or restless to sit still and others have noticed.**
   ☐ NOT AT ALL   ☐ SOME DAYS
   ☐ MORE THAN HALF THE DAYS   ☐ NEARLY EVERY DAY

7. **Trouble falling asleep or sleeping too much.**
   ☐ NOT AT ALL   ☐ SOME DAYS
   ☐ MORE THAN HALF THE DAYS   ☐ NEARLY EVERY DAY

8. **Feeling very tired or having little energy.**

   ☐ Not at all   ☐ Some days

   ☐ More than half the days   ☐ Nearly every day

9. **Trouble concentrating on reading, watching a show, etc.**

   ☐ Not at all   ☐ Some days

   ☐ More than half the days   ☐ Nearly every day

10. **Feeling nervous or anxious or on edge; worrying about a lot of different things.**

    ☐ Not at all   ☐ Some days

    ☐ More than half the days   ☐ Nearly every day

11. **Inability to control worrying. Ruminating on the same things over and over.**

    ☐ Not at all   ☐ Some days

    ☐ More than half the days   ☐ Nearly every day

12. **Muscle tension, aches, or soreness.**

    ☐ Not at all   ☐ Some days

    ☐ More than half the days   ☐ Nearly every day

13. **Becoming easily annoyed or irritable.**

    ☐ Not at all   ☐ Some days

    ☐ More than half the days   ☐ Nearly every day

Rate your level of function in the following areas from zero to 10 with zero being "not at all" and 10 being "extremely:"

- Have the above symptoms disrupted your work or school life?
- Have the above symptoms disrupted your social life?
- Have the above symptoms disrupted your family or home responsibilities?

PART I: THE DISEASE

# CHAPTER TWO
## DEPRESSION WORLDWIDE

**"You say you're 'depressed'—all I see is resilience. You are allowed to feel messed up and inside out. It doesn't mean you're defective—it just means you're human."**
—David Mitchell, British novelist, in *Cloud Atlas*

On every continent and in every nation, people suffer from depression—and many of them don't get the treatment they need. One of the most common illnesses, depression affects more than 264 million people. "Although there are known, effective treatments for mental disorders, between 76 percent and 85 percent of people in low- and middle-income countries receive no treatment for their disorder."[9]

What keeps people from seeking care for their mental illness? The reasons that rank at the top of the list are social stigma associated with mental-health disorders and inaccurate assessments by medical professionals. Other reasons include a lack of resources and trained health-care professionals. "In countries of all income levels, people who are depressed are often not correctly diagnosed, and others who do not have the disorder are too often misdiagnosed and prescribed antidepressants. The burden of depression and other mental-health conditions is on the rise globally."[10]

Even though depression is widespread around the world, a lack of support for people with depression is an international concern. According to *U.S. News and World Report*, "[o]ne thing most countries have in common is their lack of support for people with mental illness, WHO [the World Health Organization] states. 'Even in high-income countries, nearly 50 percent of people with depression do not get treatment. On average, just 3 percent of government health budgets is invested in mental health, varying from less than 1 percent in low-income countries to 5 percent in high-income countries,' the report claims."[11]

Examining the differences between nations sheds more light on that lack of support. Some of the most depressed countries are dealing with especially challenging circumstances that draw attention away from devoting resources to depression treatment. Some of the countries with the least depressed citizens don't appear to register the symptoms of depression as the disease of depression in the same way the United States does. A 2013 study in the journal *PLOS Medicine* ranked the most depressed countries. Afghanistan topped the list with more than 20 percent of the population suffering from depression. In second and third places, respectively, are Honduras and the Palestinian territories. Japan ranked as the least depressed country with a diagnosed depression rate of under 2.5 percent. However, Japan has a very high suicide rate, which calls into question the country's reported low rate of diagnosed depression.[12]

Overall, the study found the Middle East and North Africa as the most depression regions of the world. The reasons why include politics, conflict, wars, and other health epidemics, such as malaria and HIV/AIDS. Many times, efforts to help people worldwide overcome depression are hampered by culture or national norms. "Many linguistic communities, for example, in India, Korea and Nigeria, do not even have a word for 'depression', and many people from traditional societies with what may be construed as depression instead present with physical complaints such as fatigue, headache, or chest pain," writes Dr. Neel Burton, author of *Growing from Depression*. "Punjabi women who have recently immigrated to the UK and given birth find it baffling that a health visitor should pop round to check their mood: it had never crossed their minds that giving birth could be anything but a joyous event. ... Being much more exposed to the concept of depression, people in modern societies such as the UK and US are far more likely to interpret their distress in terms of depression and to seek out a diagnosis of the illness. At the same time, groups with vested interests actively promote the notion of saccharine happiness as a natural, default state, and of human distress as a mental disorder."[13]

Worldwide, the study found that "depression is the second-leading cause of disability, with slightly more than 4 percent of the world's population diagnosed with it."[14] But that number is likely higher, given the lower rates of diagnosing depression in many countries.

"Interestingly, suicide rates—which can be a marker for depression— are generally higher in more sociologically developed countries," says Dr. Robert Shulman, acting director of Rush University Medical Group in Chicago, Illinois.[15] "Globally, the rates of depression are increasing and are showing evidence of occurring at a younger age, which was a trend developing well before COVID-19."

**Global Treatments**

A research study from the University of Luxembourg and University of London that examined depression treatment in 63 countries worldwide, found that wealth is the biggest factor in whether a person who has depression can get help. "The chance of receiving treatment for depression varies strongly across countries. The same holds for the chance of receiving treatment given the presence of depressive symptoms. Country differences are partly due to compositional and contextual differences. Wealth is the most important national predictor of the chance to receive treatment. . . . We find strong cross-national variation in the chance to receive treatment for depression. Additionally, multilevel regression analyses reveal that urbanization, employment status, marital status, level of education, gender, age, and national wealth all partly explain cross-national differences in the chance to receive treatment for depression."[16]

Different cultural contexts for dealing with depression in different countries can significantly affect how depressed people perceive their health and choose their treatment. "Best studied differences in expression of depression are whether symptoms are primarily experienced in the body, or as disorders of emotions and cognitions."[17]

In the United States, a depression diagnosis usually comes with a depressed mood or a lack of pleasure in your environment. In China, people experience depression "as bodily symptoms: the person is tired and not sleeping, they don't have energy and aren't concentrating well. Historically, it's the diagnosis of *neurasthenia* (weakness of the nerves), which migrated to China from Europe via the Soviet Union. Essentially, it's major depression without the affective features."[18]

Moreover, people aren't seeking help in the same way across cultures—and that assistance isn't rendered in the same manner. In addition, the symptoms of depression aren't always labeled as such, depending on the cultural context. "Assessment is a challenge in part because many of our assessment tools are based on the [W]estern set of criteria. Because of commonalities, we might catch some symptoms, but we might also miss presentations of the disorder that look different."[19]

Some experts and scientists have begun to develop tools and treatment methods that can translate across cultures. "There is accumulating data showing that some approaches that are effective in the U.S. (e.g., cognitive-behavioral therapy) are also looking promising in other cultures. Similarly, mindfulness approaches from the East have been found to be effective in [W]estern samples."[20]

**Depression in Europe**
In Europe, depression affects a significant amount of the population, yet about half of depressed people don't get treatment for their depression, according to the WHO Regional Office for Europe. "Each year, 25% of the population suffer from depression or anxiety. Neuropsychiatric disorders account for 19.5% of the burden of disease in the European Region, and 26% in European Union (EU) countries. These disorders account for up to 40% of years lived with disability, with depression as the main cause. Up to 50% of chronic sick leaves are due to depression/anxiety. About 50% of major depressions are untreated. The cost of mood disorders and anxiety in the EU is about €170 billion per year."[21]

Depression treatment approaches differ throughout Europe. In the United Kingdom, for example, if a citizen turns up at their general practitioner's office feeling anxious, depressed, or suffering from insomnia, most likely, he will receive an antidepressant prescription. Access to psychiatry is rare and only used for cases in which the patient exhibits suicidal tendencies.[22]

In France, depression treatment also involves medications over other therapies. "Depression and anxiety are primarily considered neuroses and not psychoses and as such the psychotherapy is not covered by the health system."[23] In Germany, those suffering from depression or anxiety first stop at a general practitioner. Specialists can be called in to prescribe drugs as treatments. Psychotherapy is available for short-term sessions.[24]

Over in Spain, primary-care doctors will often treat depressed patients by prescribing anxiolytic and antidepressant drugs. Supportive psychotherapy is available too. Italian patients can go to their general practitioner or a specialist directly. "Statistics in Italy show that only 50 percent of those who suffer depression seek treatment; about 15-20 percent of these patients seek the advice of a psychiatrist. The figures are low because there is still a lot of stigma attached to seeing a health professional."[25]

Current treatment protocols in European nations are not effective enough, according to European psychiatrists Professor Eduard Vieta and Dr. Daniel Souery. "We're seeing the burden of mental-health conditions—and particularly depression—continuing to rise to become the leading cause of disease burden by 2030. With people's lifestyles becoming increasingly demanding, this is unlikely to change, leading to more people with mental-health conditions seeking medical help. However, the current infrastructure and lack of capacity within European health-care systems means that far too few patients get access to the right care at the right time," says Vieta.[26]

Some experts and medical professionals are hoping the current system will change to address this disparity. "Most primary care is delivered in a format that isn't helpful for people with mental-health conditions," says Vieta. The average patient visit of five minutes or less makes it extremely difficult to diagnoses mental health issues correctly. "As a psychiatrist, I can't effectively diagnose or help a patient with depression in just ten minutes, other than to prescribe them medication," notes Vieta. "Medication is of course important but not at the expense of a face-to-face consultation with a health-care professional."[27]

In mental health especially, there can be no one-size-fits-all approach, given individual complexities. For that reason, Vieta and Souery recommended taking a two-pronged approach to treating depression. First, providing specialist care to all patients, and second, developing or reinforcing community-support resources, including having a robust public-health system in place. "Educating people, including social workers, teachers, friends and relatives, to an adequate level would not only significantly reduce the stigma associated with mental-health conditions, but it would also help to reduce important risk factors, such as loneliness. This in turn could help to reduce the number of people who are entering the health-care system," says Souery.[28]

However, clinical practice in Europe has not kept up with innovations in neuroscience in terms of caring for those with depression. "Many of us are still relying on what we discovered over 40 years ago about neurotransmitters and the classical antidepressants like SSRIs," says Souery. "We should be exploring how to integrate genetic advances to develop personalized treatment plans or using machine learning to help predict treatment response. After all, the future is tomorrow."[29]

Integrated and comprehensive care for patients via the application of the latest sociological and educational advancements is the responsibility of all caregivers, states Vieta and Souery. They both agree that online tools can be beneficial to patients and should be employed by doctors caring for depressed patients.[30]

Overall, what's been found in Europe is that barriers to accessing new psychiatric treatments are hindering depression treatment progress. "Mental illness is one of society's greatest public-health problems and there is a vast unmet need among people of all ages. Accessing effective treatments remains an issue, as demonstrated by the example of Major Depressive Disorder (MDD), where three out of four people do not receive adequate treatment. Barriers against new psychiatric treatments during the regulatory approval and the reimbursement process may be partly to blame."[31] "We are not advancing at the right speed," Souery says. "We are still looking at depression, and treatments for depression, the old-fashioned way. The regulatory authorities are too focused on the cost of the treatment alone, instead of invested in increasing education and awareness, which is crucial."[32]

## Depression in Asia

The World Health Organization collects data on 11 different Asian nations that participate with WHO initiatives and classifies the countries as "Southeast Asia or South Asia regardless of their geographic location. These countries—Bangladesh, Bhutan, the Democratic People's Republic of Korea, India, Indonesia, Maldives, Myanmar, Nepal, Sri Lanka, Thailand, and Timor-Leste—have 86 million people who are experiencing depression, making the region home to a large majority of the world's depressed."[33]

Mental illness is considered taboo in some Southeast Asian communities, and many Asian languages don't even have a word for depression. "Professor Dinesh Bhugra, a mental-health expert at London's King's College, states that the South Asian population carries 'a bigger notion of shame' with them than other ethnic populations. South Asian religious and cultural influences often do not consider mental health a medical issue, referring to it as a 'superstitious belief.' A 2010 study by the campaign Time to Change found that South Asians rarely discuss mental health because of the risk the subject poses to their reputation and status. Discussing mental health in South Asia has yet to be socially normalized. ... Many South Asians are unable to express the specific condition of depression in their language. As a result, they often have to resort to downplaying it as part of 'life's ups and downs.' This language limitation also makes diagnoses and treatment difficult."[34]

However, some Asian nations have made encouraging progress toward expanding access to depression treatment for their citizens, and charitable organizations have also made a positive impact on mental-health care in Asia. For example, Bangladesh, Indonesia, and Sri Lanka have prioritized mental health by creating policies to focus on mental health across the nation. WHO recently applauded their work toward normalizing depression and treatment the disease, along with other mental illness. Non-governmental organizations (NGOs) also have positively impacted mental-health care, especially in nations where the government ignores mental health. "These [NGO] efforts have drastically increased the access South Asians have to mental health care. … Improving mental health in South Asia requires not only the social recognition and normalization of depression and mental illness but the continued action of both government and non-government programs. With increased access to mental health care and support in South Asia, the expansive issues of poverty and illness will be positively affected."[35]

A research study published in the *Asia-Pacific Psychiatry* journal examined depression in the Asian nations of China, Hong Kong, India, Indonesia, Japan, Korea, Malaysia, Singapore, Taiwan, and Thailand. The study found that economic income levels affected how depressed people expressed their symptoms. "The most common presentations of depressive symptoms were persistent sadness, loss of interest, and insomnia. Similar findings were found regardless of the region, country, or its income level … This study demonstrates that in Asia, despite variations in the initial symptom reported by the patients, across different countries/territories, core depressive symptoms remain the same."[36]

### Depression in Australia

Depression treatments are more openly communicated about in Australian society, and people tend to have access to care if they pursue it. "In Australia, it's estimated that 45 percent of people will experience a mental health condition in their lifetime. In any one year, around 1 million Australian adults have depression, and over 2 million have anxiety."[37] Annually, approximately 6 percent of all Australian adults are affected by depression.[38]

The Australian Government Department of Health stated in a report that lifestyle changes, medication, and counseling therapy are all recommended depression treatments for Australians. "Whatever the severity of a person's depression, treatment should include learning new skills like problem solving and changes to lifestyle, like cutting down on stress, increasing exercise and physical fitness and not using alcohol or other drugs. If the depression is moderate to severe, then two main treatments can be considered, antidepressant medication and psychological therapy."[39]

Depressed people in Australia are encouraged to get an assessment from their general practitioner doctor (GP) or a counselor, then work with him or her to create a depression treatment plan. Such plans might include use of medication, specific psychological therapy or a mixture of both. GPs also suggest specialists for more treatment or hospital admission for severe cases of depression.[40]

In Australia, depression treatments can be grouped into three categories: individual therapy, medication, or community support programs.

- "Individual therapy—a doctor, psychologist, or other health professional talks with the person about their symptoms, and discusses alternative ways of thinking about and managing them.
- Medication—antidepressant medications may also help control the symptoms of depression.
- Community support programs—this support should include information, accommodation, help with finding suitable work, training and education, psychosocial rehabilitation and mutual support groups. Understanding and acceptance by the community is also very important."[41]

**Depression in South America**
Depressed people living in South American nations often lack access to treatment because of poor care coordination or because they don't seek care due to mental-health stigmas. "Depression is the most common mental illness in the world. In Latin America, 5 percent of the adult population suffers from it, but most neither seek—nor receive—treatment, according to the World Health Organization (WHO). ... 'These illnesses have an impact on the daily lives of individuals: their work, cognitive abilities, studies, family and social activities,' says Dr. José Miguel Uribe, a psychiatrist and World Bank consultant."[42]

In Pan America, severe depression impacts 12.5 percent of the population, according to a study from the Pan American Health Organization (PAHO). Services for these people tends to be fragmented with a lack of coordination between levels of healthcare. The low health budgets allocated to psychiatric hospitals in Mexico, Latin Caribbean, Central America, and South America "show a negligence and lack of relevance that is given to mental health in Latin America from government budgets that do not cover enough institutions that treat mental disorders."[43]

The PAHO noted in a report that "[i]n terms of burden and prevalence, depression continues to be the leading mental disorder and is twice as frequent in women as in men. From 10 percent to 15 percent of women in industrialized countries and from 20 percent to 40 percent of women in developing countries suffer from depression during pregnancy or the postpartum period."[44]

Widespread poverty in many Latin American countries means many people cannot afford treatment for depression. "People living in poverty have more limited access to adequate mental health care, thereby worsening the vicious cycle of inequality in Latin American countries. 'There is a clear relationship between standard of living and common mental disorders,' says Paulo Rossi Menezes, a professor of medicine at the University of Sao Paulo. The poor are at greater risk of suffering a mental illness such as depression because they face more difficulties in life and because they have less access to appropriate care."[45]

In addition to poverty, stigmas related to mental health may prevent South Americans from pursuing depression treatment. "This makes it much more difficult for people to seek help because they feel ashamed or are concerned about the treatments. This attitude may be partly due to a lack of information. 'People have no information and this contributes to the obstacles to care,' says Menezes. 'People do not know that what they are feeling could be what we call depression, or if they do recognize it, they may have a hard time telling others about it.'"[46]

Some commonly identified myths in Latin America about people with mental-health issues include that they are aggressive, dangerous, and violent; are likely to exhibit bizarre behavior; won't be able to get better;

should be alone or away from the public; and can't perform the same tasks or activities as everyone else.[47] Specific parts of Latin American culture can positively influence how mental health is perceived. For example, *Familismo*—the culture value of the family as a unit—can aid mental health. "Some researchers claim that this value is associated with increased rates of emotional closeness and openness within the family, which may reduce the impact of mental health stigma."[48]

On the flip side, *Familismo* also can be a source of discrimination against people with mental-health disorders in Latin American countries. "Examples of negative family factors include hostile attitudes from family and extended family, as well as family members underestimating someone's abilities. Another study found that most Latin and Hispanic families would deny the presence of depression or another mental health condition in a family member unless they were unable to cope or the symptoms of the condition were life threatening. In the same study, many of the survey participants believed that children's mental health conditions are due to the sinful behaviors of their parents."[49]

Sometimes, *Familismo* leads people to conceal their mental-health struggles to protect others in their families, who can in turn discourage members from seeking treatment, adhering to a prescribed medications, or attending therapy. Furthermore, some Latin American cultures may shy away from discussing mental-health issues.

Faith may play a key role in the perceptions surrounding mental illness in Latin America. "This makes sense, given that these communities tend to rely on religious institutions as an important spiritual, educational, and social resource."[50]

People in South American nations are working to strengthen care for depressed people through strategies like strengthening general health care, including the treatment of mental health. "This means making services available near the people, in the communities, and also assuring that general medical staff are trained to recognize mental illnesses. ... Fortunately, things are changing in some Latin American countries. In Brazil, for example, while 20 or 30 years ago, the focus was mainly on serious mental illness and patients in psychiatric hospitals, it has now been expanded ... [with a goal] to extend service access to people who may be suffering from less severe mental disorders, like most cases of depression."[51]

## Depression in Africa

A review of research from throughout Africa from King's College London, Addis Ababa University, and Brighton and Sussex Medical School stated that the prevalence of depression in African nations ranges from "at around 10 - 20 percent of the population at any one time" and "most people living with depression go untreated."[52]

A research study from *The Lancet* medical journal stated that there's not enough depression research being conducted in Africa, nor enough treatment for Africans who are depressed. "The scarcity of research mirrors the weakness of mental health services on the continent and the blind eye turned to the problem by many Africans and their governments. Worldwide, 24 percent of countries that reported to the WHO's 2014 Mental Health Atlas survey did not have or had not implemented standalone mental health policies; in Africa, this proportion rose to 46 percent."[53]

Part of the disconnect between those suffering from depression and the ability to receive treatment stems from the perception of depression in African cultures. "Depression was perceived as problem with its roots in social adversity. ... Self-help and community resources were the first line in addressing depression. Traditional and biomedical medicine were used when symptoms were chronic or severe. Stepped care interventions should take into account local resources and models."[54]

An *Africa Renewal* article referred to "an epidemic of mental illness on the continent."[55] A snapshot of some African countries gives a dismal picture. "[H]health experts have estimated that a fourth of the Kenyan population of 44 million suffers from a range of mental diseases, including schizophrenia and other psychotic disorders, bipolar disorder, depression and severe anxiety."[56] Around three-fourths of mentally ill South Africans can't access therapeutic or psychiatric care. "The WHO estimates that fewer than 10 percent of mentally ill Nigerians have access to a psychiatrist or health worker, because there are only 130 psychiatrists in the country of 174 million people."[57]

In 2012, Ghana passed the Mental Health Act, becoming a pioneer in describing its mental-illness policy. "Early that year a report by Human Rights Watch (HRW), a non-governmental organization, estimated that 2.8 million Ghanaians (out of a population of 25.9 million) had mental illness."[58]

Poorer African countries have an even worse picture of mental health, especially those embroiled in recent or current civil wars and conflict, such as Sierra Leone and Liberia. A century ago, Sierra Leone had been a pioneer in mental health on the continent with the British-established Kissy Mental Home, now the Kissy National Referral Psychiatric Hospital. The hospital is still the country's lone psychiatric hospital.[59]

In Africa, the widespread belief that "mentally ill patients brought the disease upon themselves by using illicit drugs may be one reason African governments do not prioritize mental health. Experts have also pointed to a tendency in Africa to view acute mental health diseases as supernatural afflictions that can be cured only through spiritual or traditional medicinal interventions. Families of the mentally ill often turn for a cure to these interventions, or to 'prayer camps'—retreats where the sick person is often chained to trees and prayed for. This practice is especially prevalent in Nigeria."[60]

Some of those who most visibly suffer from mental illnesses are the homeless, which adds to the stigma of mental illness. Vagrancy is considered a crime in many African nations and mentally ill homeless persons often find themselves chained in mental-health hospital "prisons."[61]

The outlook for depression treatments in Africa is grim. "Mental health problems appear to be increasing in importance in Africa. Between 2000 and 2015 the continent's population grew by 49 percent, yet the number of years lost to disability as a result of mental and substance use disorders increased by 52 percent. In 2015, 17.9 million years were lost to disability as a consequence of mental health problems."[62]

With Africa's population forecast to double between 2020 and 2050, the pressures on young residents who already struggle to find work will likely increase. "Many will experience psychological problems as they fail to realize their ambitions, and some will turn to substance misuse as a means of alleviating their frustration."[63]

# CHAPTER THREE
## DEPRESSION'S STIGMA

**"I think this man might be useful to me—if my black dog returns. He seems quite away from me now—it is such a relief. All the [colors] come back into the picture."**
—Winston Churchill, prime minister of the United Kingdom (1940 to 1945, 1951 to 1955), in a letter to his wife

Not only do depressed people suffer from the health effects of the disease, they also often suffer from the stigma of having depression in American society. Cultural stereotypes about depression, which are often reinforced by mainstream media, still fuel negative attitudes toward people with the condition. The stigma of depression as a personal weakness rather than a legitimate medical condition persists despite efforts by those who treat depressed patients to educate the public. However, the stigma seems to be lessening as people who live with the condition—including public figures and celebrities—speak up about their own experiences with depression.

Because of the complex nature of depression, the stigmatization of those with the disease has led to discrimination and other injustices. Depression affects a person's identity and ability to communicate, which in turn can create difficulties in getting help and contribute to social isolation and reinforce damaging societal perceptions. "It [stigmatizing] can lead to feelings of guilt, anger, and anxiety, and is a pervasive phenomenon. Stigma can come from family members, from work colleagues, from health care professionals, educators, and members of the general community."[64]

In general, stigma envelopes the negative response of society toward a perceived flaw in someone's personal character. That perception can result in discrimination and prejudice against the individual. The stigma related to depression has been lessening of late, but it's still quite common for those with depression to experience bias and judgment.[65]

## A Result of Personal Weakness

The main assumption that contributes to the stigma of depression is that the disease is somehow a character flaw, a personal weakness in those who suffer from it. This attitude can result in the mistreatment of people with depression. "Two thousand years of humiliation, mistrust, outcasting, punishment, and general antipathy will leave its effect on how we currently feel about people with depression."[66]

Because of this historical stigma, people suffering from depression are not encouraged to "put their hands up and identify themselves with a history of supposed malingerers, sinners, sexual miscreants, and lazy and self-obsessed serial complainers, who drain the personal and financial resources of others."[67] Depression has become linked to a sense that those with depression could be threatening or objectionable to interact with, as well as somehow liable for having the disease in the first place.[68]

During my last major depressive episode, which happened when I was chairman of my family's company, I struggled but held it together for the most part. But I was a little paranoid about how people were viewing me, asking myself: "Do they see any symptoms?" Of course, this is something you're not sharing with anybody. You end up walking around thinking that people might be picking up on the fact that you're acting a little different. And you also wonder how people would react if they knew the truth—that you are someone who suffers from depression.

But that mindset is slowly changing. DestinyBlue, a London-based artist who suffers from depression, uses her art to show what the disease feels like. Her emotionally charged, colorful, and imaginative art conveys depression in a vivid form. "I didn't come from an expressive household, and here I was with so much inside me—so much I didn't understand, thoughts, feelings, and emotions marched through me like an invading army," says DestinyBlue in an August 2017 interview with HuffPost.[69] "I needed a way to process and vent, and drawing provided a canvas to untangle myself upon."

As DestinyBlue shares how crippling depression can be to its sufferers through her words and art, she's helping to unravel the mystery of mental illness and giving people a glimpse of a better tomorrow. "I want others who are also struggling with mental health issues to know there is hope, and that they are not alone, and that someone else understands how tough a path it is to walk, and how strong you are for carrying on," she explains in the HuffPost interview.

## A Result of Personal Choices

Society's stigma against depression as a personal weakness also implies that somehow the people who suffer from depression made decisions that led to their depression, which means they must be personally at fault for being depressed. Even though medical knowledge has now progressed to the point where it's clear that biological changes to people's brains play key roles in depression, public perception often characterizes people with depression as somehow being to blame for their condition.

Since the turn of the twenty-first century, scientific evidence has emerged that shows depression's roots "in a malfunctioning brain, not unlike many other neurological disorders. But although brain disorders such as Alzheimer's disease, Parkinson's disease, and stroke may be viewed with compassion, a mental illness such as depression is too often seen as a sign of personal weakness."[70] (See Chapter 14 for more on treatments and understanding of depression in the twenty-first century.)

Efforts by family, friends, and employers to "try to shake the sufferer out of their depressive stupor … are usually about as effective as telling a heart attack or stroke victim to 'run it off'."[71] These comments are singularly unhelpful because depression is not a life choice. Depressed people can't simply *choose* not to be depressed.

Anyone can develop depression, regardless of their personal choices in life. "The history of our family shows we are the poster family for depression," says my sister Shawn Stratman.[72] "That's why when we talk about it, we're just so sad because it's an evil disease. It takes your joy. I hope it's less misunderstood now."

## Depression Portrayals

It's no secret that the way the mainstream media, including television shows, movies, and the Internet, portrays different groups of people influences how many Americans regard those groups. Unfortunately for people with depression, the media has often portrayed them in negative ways that perpetuate the stigma of depression as a personal weakness.

For example, television news programs and newspaper articles often stress a history of mental illness when describing a violent criminal's background. In addition, comedians use those with mental illness as fodder for jokes, while pharmaceutical company advertisements often exaggerate mental-illness images to push their products.[73]

Movies play an influential role in shaping how Americans think about depression. "Hollywood films can perpetuate curious beliefs regarding the mental illness spectrum. ... The victims of mental illness are often portrayed as aggressive, unpredictable, and dangerous, with psychiatrists commonly essayed as inept or manipulative."[74]

When the media does portray depressed people in positive ways as normal people, it can help lessen negative stereotypes. "Ironically, the media are also powerful partners for eradicating stigma. Education is the antidote to inaccurate beliefs and unfair behavior. By presenting depression as just another illness—and a very common and treatable one at that—the media can have a major impact on public opinion."[75]

One famous person from the twentieth century who struggled with depression is Winston Churchill. Born into a politically prominent family, Churchill suffered from depression all his life. His father, Lord Randolph Churchill, the eighth Duke of Marlborough, had psychotic episodes, and his daughter Diana eventually committed suicide after having had major depressive episodes throughout her life.[76]

Some scholars credit Churchill's experience with depression—which he called his "black dog"—as the force behind his drive to equip England against the growing threat of fascism in Germany prior to World War II. As psychiatrist and historian Anthony Storr points out, "Only a man who knew what it was to discern a gleam of hope in a hopeless situation, whose courage was beyond reason and whose aggressive spirit burned at its fiercest when he was hemmed in and surrounded by enemies, could have given emotional reality to the words of defiance which rallied and sustained us in the menacing summer of 1940."[77] (See "Depression Can Affect Anyone" on page 45 for a partial list of famous people with depression.)

### Discouraging Treatment

Unfortunately, depressed people who are embarrassed or ashamed about their mental-health condition sometimes choose not to seek treatment. And if depressed people do start treatment but then feel stigmatized for doing so, they may discontinue treatment.

For my father's generation and older generations, the image of insane asylums (especially as depicted in the movie "One Flew Over the Cuckoo's Nest") as awful places where crazy people were locked up is still vivid. "Those memories put depression in a category you don't talk about," says my father, Dick Litzsinger.[78] "It was something you hid in public. That's the reason, over time, that these seminars Mark does at Rush University Medical Center in Chicago, Illinois, and books like this will go a long way to dispelling that silence. These measures will get people able to talk about it."

A celebrity feud between actor Tom Cruise and actress Brooke Shields in 2005 drew the public's attention to the ongoing misconceptions about depression. Cruise criticized Shields during a television interview with Matt Lauer on the NBC show "Today" for taking an antidepressant medication for her postpartum depression, asserting that she shouldn't need to rely on a drug to treat depression. Cruise basically said that there is no such thing as a chemical imbalance and that Shields could simply exercise and eat a nutritious diet to make her depression go away.

Shields responded in an op-ed piece for the *New York Times* called

"War of Words." In the article, Shields writes that she felt "compelled to speak not just for myself but also for the hundreds of thousands of women who have suffered from postpartum depression."[79] Adding that, "to suggest that I was wrong to take drugs to deal with my depression, and that instead I should have taken vitamins and exercised shows an utter lack of understanding about postpartum depression and childbirth in general. If any good can come of Mr. Cruise's ridiculous rant, let's hope that it gives much-needed attention to a serious disease."[80]

In the workplace, companies are also beginning to destigmatize mental illness by drafting policies that encourage employees to take time off work to address issues like depression and anxiety. A *Wall Street Journal* article touted several such companies, like Ernst & Young, American Express Co., and Prudential Financial, which offered employee-assistance programs, onsite access to mental-health professionals, and free counseling.[81]

## A Fresh View

When public figures share their personal struggles with depression, it can offer hope to others and bring discussions about depression and its stigma to the forefront of our cultural dialogue for a time.

Shields, who also chronicled her battle with depression in *Down Came the Rain: My Journey Through Postpartum Depression*, writes that as a celebrity, she was making an intentional effort to try to decrease society's stigma of people who suffer from depression. In the op-ed article, Shields notes she had heard from many other depressed people who felt stigmatized, stating: "Since writing about my experiences with the disease, I have been approached by many women who have told me their stories and thanked me for opening up about a topic that is often not discussed because of fear, shame, or lack of support and information. Experts estimate that one in ten women suffer, usually in silence, with this treatable disease."[82]

The most powerful public reaction to the stigma of depression in recent years came about after the death of actor Robin Williams in 2014. Although Williams had been depressed for many years, he hadn't publicly spoken much about it. His suicide caused widespread shock and prompted discussion about depression in both mainstream and social media.

The reaction may have been especially powerfully in Williams' case because of the sharp dichotomy between his public face and private one. Publicly, Williams was known for making people laugh with his brilliant and outlandish comedy. Privately, Williams struggled with depression and substance abuse. In addition, an autopsy revealed that he suffered from Lewy body dementia, which causes hallucinations and disorientation.[83]

The shock of his death by suicide provided a needed wake-up call to everyone that mental illness is an oppressive force. "As the public registered the finality of his absence, social media became an outlet not only for heartfelt remembrances, but also messages of hope and compassion. This widespread empathy, matched by private conversations around the dinner table and water cooler, is a new phenomenon that demonstrates just how much the stigma of suicide has diminished in recent years."[84]

Author J.C. Arkham was among those who shared personal experiences with depression after Williams' death. In his book *Claims Department: Robin Williams Memorial: Comedian, Actor, Legend*, Arkham writes: "This man's sense of humor got me through all the tough times growing up. It was like losing an uncle I dearly loved. There's nothing okay about this. However, I do understand his battle with depression. I don't just say that as a cliché. I suffered from severe depression for many years. Almost no one knew. Like him, I was good at hiding it (well, y'all know now). ... It hurts me profoundly to the core that he couldn't make it over to 'the other side.' I was on that precipice. I feel lucky I have people in my life who kept me from taking that step off."[85]

**Stamp Out the Stigma**

All of us can contribute to the end of the stigma associated with depression. Yes, strides have been made to eradicate the shame of depression from American society, but too many lives have been lost for us to continue this slow journey. More of us need to join the effort to educate the public about depression.

The responsibility for changing the negative perceptions about depression to a more benign view rests on all of us—family, friends, coworkers, acquaintances, and communities. "By learning about depression and passing the knowledge along, we can all help replace fear and rejection with understanding and respect."[86]

As human beings, we must help each other to better understand this disease. Education is the key to learning the facts about the illness and rising above the stigma it currently has. Once depression is understood by the masses, society can help itself by making information and resources available so no one has to suffer like I and others have over the centuries.

## Depression Can Affect Anyone

When famous people speak out about their own struggles with depressive disorders, it goes a long way to removing the stigma of the disease. Here is a partial list of famous people throughout history who have struggled with depression.[87]

- John Adams,* second president of the United States
- Buzz Aldrin, American astronaut
- Hans Christian Andersen,* Danish children's author
- Roseanne Barr, comedian
- Ludwig van Beethoven,* German composer
- Ingmar Bergman, Swedish film director
- Beyoncé, American singer
- Terry Bradshaw, former Pittsburgh Steelers quarterback
- Marlon Brando, actor
- Barbara Bush, former first lady of the United States
- Truman Capote, American writer
- Jim Carrey, actor and comedian
- Johnny Carson, American television host
- Agatha Christie, English mystery writer
- Winston Churchill, former British Prime Minister
- Calvin Coolidge, thirtieth president of the United States
- Sheryl Crow, singer

- John Daly, professional golfer
- Charles Darwin,* British naturalist
- Diana, Princess of Wales
- Charles Dickins,* English author
- Emily Dickinson,* American poet
- Lady Gaga, American singer/songwriter
- Ernest Hemingway, Pulitzer Prize-winning novelist
- Audrey Hepburn, British actress
- Samuel Johnson,* British lexicographer
- Stephen King, American novelist
- Abraham Lincoln, sixteenth president of the United States.
- Mary Todd Lincoln, former first lady of the United States
- Greg Louganis, American Olympic medal-winning diver
- Michelangelo,* Italian painter and sculptor
- Marilyn Monroe, American actress
- Wolfgang Amadeus Mozart,* Austrian composer
- Sir Isaac Newton,* English scientist
- Friedrich Nietzsche,* German philosopher
- Edgar Allan Poe, American poet and writer
- John D. Rockefeller, American industrialist
- Charles Spurgeon, English preacher
- Leo Tolstoy, Russian novelist
- Mark Twain, American writer
- Vincent van Gogh,* Impressionist painter
- Robin Williams, American actor and comedian
- Oprah Winfrey, American talk show host
- Boris Yeltsin, first president of Russia

*Historical research supports these persons as having suffered from some form of depression.

# CHAPTER FOUR

## DEPRESSION'S IMPACT ON CHILDREN, TEENS AND COLLEGE STUDENTS

**"A big part of depression is feeling really lonely, even if you're in a room full of a million people."**
—Lilly Singh, Canadian comedian

Depression throws turmoil into the lives of children, teens, and young adults who suffer from it. During a season of life when they're growing and their brains are developing, it is particularly stressful for youth to struggle with depression. "We need to understand that depression in youth looks differently," says Deborahanne Reimer, a licensed clinical professional counselor certified in alcohol and drug counseling who works with young people at a Chicago, Illinois, high school. "Depression in youth often manifests as irritability and anger, which is easily overlooked as typical teenage behavior."[88]

Caring parents, teachers, coaches, and others who recognize signs of depression in the young people they know can reach out to help. Children, teens, and college students who get the diagnoses and treatment they need can enter adulthood with a stronger foundation, prepared to launch their lives as adults without being crippled by the disease.

Although youth may seem like a carefree time, it's also a time when some people first experience depression. "About 5 percent of children and adolescents in the general population suffer from depression at any given point in time," according to the American Academy of Child & Adolescent

Psychiatry. "Children under stress, who experience loss, or who have attentional, learning, conduct or anxiety disorders are at a higher risk for depression. Depression also tends to run in families."[89]

The older youth become, it seems, the more likely they are to start experiencing depression. "Depression occurs at a rate of about 2% during childhood and from 4%–7% during adolescence,"[90] according to an article on MedicineNet.com. The article adds that "depression is common during the teenage years, affecting about 20% of adolescents by the time they reach adulthood."[91]

The increased use of social media has been linked to higher incidents of depression among young people. "There's been an actual increase in depression in emerging adults (those between the ages of 18 and 29)," says Dr. Crystal I. Lee, a licensed psychologist and owner of LA Concierge Psychologist in Los Angeles, California. "With my clients and from research, usage of Instagram, Facebook, and other social media correlates with more depressive symptoms and decreased overall mental health."[92]

According to the National Institute of Mental Health, "in 2015, an estimated 3 million adolescents aged 12 to 17 in the United States had at least one major depressive episode in the past year. This number represented 12.5 percent of the U.S. population aged 12 to 17."[93] Contrast that with the statistics for depression among adults aged 18 years and beyond: "In 2015, an estimated 16.1 million adults aged 18 or older in the United States had at least one major depressive episode in the past year. This number represented 6.7 percent of all U.S. adults."[94] A greater percentage of the adolescent population suffers from depression than does the adult population, including college students.

A recent study of depression among teen girls showed that "depression in many children appears to start as early as age 11. By the time they hit age 17, the analysis found, 13.6 percent of boys and a staggering 36.1 percent of girls have been or are depressed. These numbers are significantly higher than previous estimates."[95]

It makes sense for adults who are concerned about the young people they love to pay close attention when those children and teens seem depressed, and to intervene to help when needed. "As much as we've made strides—significant strides in mental health issues—there still [is] quite a bit of stigma and stain surrounding all of that," says Dr. Lee. "A lot of the clients I work with start to isolate from others, which feeds depression and anxiety, because of the shame of experiencing depressive symptoms. The more we can encourage those who need help to get help, the better quality of life they will experience."

## Depressive Triggers

Although the suspected causes of depression at any age are complex—and range from chemical imbalances in people's brains to stress in their environment—some risk factors in particular seem to contribute to depression among youth. These factors include the stress of change and uncertainty, changes in developing brains, and substance abuse.

Young people frequently experience change in their lives, and they're often uncertain about what will happen to them as a result of that change. Some of those changes might include switching schools, a family move, starting or stopping extracurricular activities, and evolving friendships.

As children, teens, and young adults learn more about who they are as people and discover what they want to do with their lives, questions and uncertainties will arise that could impact their mental health.

"The increase in social media, the decrease in authentic conversations, and the loud voice in their heads, plus everyone's expectations and ideas of what 'happy' is has fed into clinical depression among our youth," says Lynn R Zakeri, LCSW, who has a private practice in the Chicago area. "There's always been sadness but now we hear about it a lot more."[96]

All that change and uncertainty may lead to depression, especially among young adults. According to LiveScience.com, "Young adults are saying goodbye to childhood and adolescence, and trying to make their own way while dealing with frequent change and uncertainty, which could trigger feelings of sadness and irritability. Going off into the world, establishing a clear identity, developing a capacity for intimate relationships, and forming a foundation to build a future career and adult life are all part of the challenges to people in their twenties that could make them vulnerable to depression, said Dr. Stuart Goldman, a child and adolescent psychiatrist at Boston Children's Hospital."[97]

The stress of both personal and professional changes may contribute to young adults developing depression, according to an article from Child Trends/DataBank Indicator. That article noted, "Young adulthood, defined here as between the ages of 18 and 29, is a time of great change for many people, and has been associated with greater risk of mental health problems and higher levels of social stress."[98]

Dr. Lee adds, "Many of today's emerging adults have no resiliency, and have been thrust into a more stressful environment without coping skills. That's another reason why we're seeing more mental health issues with college students."

Some of those changes include starting to work in unrewarding jobs and dealing with the challenges of getting married and starting families. "Unemployment and unrewarding job environments, such as those characterized by few low-level cognitive demands, minimal skills, and little autonomy (common features of many entry-level jobs), have been linked with depression among young adults,"[99] the Child Trends/DataBank Indicator article says. In addition, it states: "While positive aspects of marriage often serve to protect against depression, new financial burdens, career demands, a poor adjustment to married life, and the birth of children among young couples can also lead to negative mental health outcomes, especially among women."[100]

Brain development that happens during the teen and early adult years also has been identified as a possible cause of depression when the disease is somehow triggered during the maturation process. As LiveScience.com says, "those in their early 20s are dealing with these challenges before their brain is fully mature. The prefrontal cortex—the part of the brain involved in reasoning and controlling —finishes developing about age 25. Most people who have a genetic vulnerability to depression, typically experience their first episode of the condition between ages 14 and 24."[101]

Substance abuse—especially involving alcohol, cigarettes, and opioid drugs—also seems to be a risk factor for depression among youth. The Child Trends/DataBank Indicator article noted that "young adulthood coincides with the legal age for alcohol use. Young adults who engage in frequent drinking, or who smoke cigarettes, are more likely to experience depression."[102]

"Teens and young adults turn to alcohol to self-medicate," says Deborahanne Reimer. "Often in college, drinking alcohol is overlooked as a symptom of depression because of the perception that everybody drinks in college. Our culture has created this disguise that hides identifying the problem of depression, and substance abuse is often used as a band-aid."

Opioid addiction, an epidemic in the United States, has also been linked to depression as a possible cause of the disease. Opioids are often prescribed to control pain. Youth who may at first take an opioid medication for pain relief (such as while recovering from an injury) may become addicted to that medication and continue to take it on a long-term basis. By doing so, they may make themselves vulnerable to depression.

According to a PsychCentral.com article, "New research suggests that while opioids may cause a short-term improvement in mood, long-term use increases the chance of depression."[103] That article cites research from Saint Louis University in Missouri, noting that "long-term opioid use of more than 30 days can lead to changes in neuroanatomy and low testosterone, among other possible biological explanations."[104] Further, "the relationship between opioid drugs and depression was independent of the known contribution of pain to depression. Accordingly, the study calls on clinicians to consider the contribution of opioid use when depressed mood develops in their patients."[105]

The good news is that some factors appear to help protect young people from developing depression. According to MedicineNet.com, "protective factors for teen depression include having the involvement of supportive adults, strong family and peer relationships, healthy coping skills, and skills in emotion regulation."[106]

## Home Contributions

When children experience persistent feelings of loneliness, those emotions may make them more vulnerable to developing depression than kids who enjoy loving relationships with friends and family. Likewise, if parents fail to provide a warm, caring home environment for children, their kids may be more prone to depression. "Children who struggle with ongoing loneliness may be … more likely to be sad, disconnected and worried. … These negative feelings combined with continued isolation can lead to depression and anxiety."[107]

A recent study of adolescent girls who were involved in child-welfare agency cases found that lonely young people were likely to be depressed, depressed youth were likely to be lonely, and youth who experienced depression and/or loneliness were likely to be falling behind in school and lacking hope for their future. These "findings suggest that there are statistically significant and fairly substantial bidirectional relationships between loneliness and depression or depression-related factors that include school disengagement and low expectations for the future."[108]

Depressed adults who didn't receive enough emotional support from their parents growing up may have been affected by that lack of support in a way that contributed to them developing depression later, another study revealed. Researchers at New York's University of Albany and the University of Michigan in Ann Arbor "found a lack of parental support during childhood is associated with increased levels of depressive symptoms and chronic health conditions (such as hypertension, arthritis, and urinary problems) in adulthood, and this association persists with increasing age throughout adulthood into early old age."[109]

These connections between loneliness and depression show the importance of parents, teachers, and other caring adults reaching out to youth who seem lonely. The Albany/Michigan study of adolescent girls advised several ways that parents and other caring adults can try to help lonely young people: "In order to help prevent depression, school disengagement, or low expectations for the future, a variety of interventions can address loneliness. Such interventions include enhancing peer or family relationships, for example, or promoting participation in pro-social activities (e.g., sports, clubs at school, youth groups in the community). These network-enhancing strategies can help to introduce or develop potentially close connections that prevent or counteract loneliness in order to avert depression or depression-related factors."[110]

Loving parents are especially important to help prevent depression.

A University of California-Los Angeles (UCLA) study suggests that relationships between parents and children may alter neural circuits in children that affect their health throughout their lifetimes—including their risk of developing depression. Emotionally cold parent-child relationships led to a greater risk of mental and physical health problems for the children, while loving parent-child relationships led to better health.[111]

The study points out "that a loving relationship may also prevent the rise in biomarkers indicative of disease risk across numerous physiological systems, impacting adverse health outcomes decades later. … The UCLA findings suggest that parental warmth and affection protect one against the harmful effects of toxic childhood stress."[112]

### Helicopter Parenting

Helicopter parents—those who are either overprotective of their children or excessively involved in their children's lives—intend to try to protect their children from suffering. Ironically, though, helicopter parents often end up achieving the exact opposite: causing unnecessary suffering for their children. A tragic example of this is the link between helicopter parenting and depression. "College-aged students whose parents are overly involved in their academic lives, or whose parents created rigidly structured childhood environments, are more likely to experience anxiety and depression. … They may also experience academic difficulties."[113]

Kirsten Li-Barber, assistant professor of psychology at High Point University in North Carolina, discusses research that shows helicopter parenting may contribute to depression in a ChicagoTribune.com article: "Research of teens with overprotective parents … has found they are more anxious, less socially skilled, have poorer coping skills and higher rates of depression. In addition, they don't transition to college well."[114]

How can helicopter parenting lead to depression in youth? A possible answer could be that such parents squelch young people's developmental needs to build competence through autonomy. A study of college students revealed that "students who reported having over-controlling parents reported significantly higher levels of depression and less satisfaction with life. Furthermore, the negative effects of helicopter parenting on college students' well-being were largely explained by the perceived violation of students' basic psychological needs for autonomy and competence. ... Lower levels of competence were related to higher levels of depression and lower levels of satisfaction with life. Additionally, lower perceived autonomy was associated with more depression. More specifically, helicopter behaviors were shown to have significant indirect effects on both depression and life satisfaction through competence as well as an indirect effect on depression through autonomy."[115]

The study elaborated on the process, noting that "students who feel as if they are being 'helicoptered' also feel that their basic psychological needs are not being met. When parents engage in controlling behaviors, students' sense of personal autonomy may be diminished. Feeling a lack of volition and control can lead to depression."[116]

In her book *How to Raise an Adult: Break Free of the Overparenting Trap and Prepare Your Kid for Success*, Julie Lythcott-Haims comments that "the research shows that figuring out for themselves is a critical element to people's mental health. Your kids have to be there for *themselves*. That's a harder truth to swallow when your kid is in the midst of a problem or worse, a crisis, but taking the long view, it's the best medicine for them."[117]

Helicopter parents who want to change their parental style to reduce the risk of their children developing depression can simply start to pull back as their kids grow older. "Parenting experts say you need to imprint solid values—like honesty and a work ethic—and then get out of the way when your children become teenagers, grow up, and start making their own decisions—and deal with the consequences, for better or worse."[118]

### The Pandemic's Impact

The coronavirus pandemic, which started in early 2020, exacerbated the mental-health struggles that young people already faced pre-pandemic. The prolonged isolation, at-home schooling, and the increased stress because of COVID-19 (the illness caused by the coronavirus) contributed to a significant rise in depression among young people, from children to teens to young adults.

Although children and teens were less likely than other age groups to become seriously physically sick with COVID-19, they were still vulnerable to the virus. Social distancing became a vital part of controlling the spread of the deadly virus. Many schools closed, forcing youth worldwide into lockdowns at home and virtual schooling. In-person socializing with their friends presented serious risks, so many children and teens relied on virtual contact methods to stay in touch remotely. When some schools reopened, children and teens dealt with the stress of uncertainty over their safety as well as socially distancing in classrooms. In addition, schools frequently changed their plans to accommodate new information from local, state, and federal health organizations. Online learning presented its own challenges, such as distraction and lack of motivation among many students from kindergarten through college. Academic grades dropped and school activities evaporated.

These social restrictions, added stressors, and less face-to-face time with friends or activities caused sadness among some young people. "I felt like I was trapped in my own little house and everyone was far away," says a 14-year-old boy in a November 2020 *New York Times* article. "When you're with friends, you're completely distracted and you don't think about the bad stuff going on. During quarantine, I was so alone. All the sad things I used to brush off, I realized I couldn't brush them off anymore. ... Being in another person's presence makes you feel OK. When I can't see my friends, I feel like the world is caving in."[119]

During the pandemic, already depressed young people struggled even more, and some who had previously enjoyed good mental health became depressed for the first time. As noted earlier in this chapter, depression had reached epidemic proportions among young people even before the pandemic. As an NPR.org article noted, "Even before the coronavirus hit, mental health problems such as depression and anxiety were on the rise in children ages 6 to 17, according to the Centers for Disease Control and Prevention. Research shows social isolation can make these symptoms worse."[120]

Studies conducted during the pandemic showed high rates of depression in young people. A National Institutes of Health study uncovered "high rates of anxiety, depression, and post-traumatic symptoms" among children and adolescents. "Posttraumatic, anxiety, and depression disorders are expected during and [in the] aftermath of the pandemic. Some groups, like children, have more susceptibility to having long term consequences in mental health."[121]

The NPR.org article reveals that a survey of more than 3,000 U.S. teens "found nearly a third reporting they were unhappy and depressed 'much more than usual' in the past month. Almost 51 percent said they felt a lot more uncertainty about the future as well."[122] In addition, a survey of parents in Italy and Spain found "nearly 86% reported changes in their children such as difficulty concentrating and spending more time online and asleep, and less time engaging in physical activity" and a study of children in China "found that anxiety and depression rose compared with rates seen in previous investigations."[123]

Formal research is still being conducted as the pandemic progresses, but NPR.org note that "There's plenty of anecdotal evidence to corroborate these trends."[124] Saun-Toy Trotter, a psychotherapist at University of California, San Francisco Benioff Children's Hospital, says in the NPR.org article that she has seen "high levels of depression" since the pandemic began and that her clinic recorded more youth suicide attempts in the first four weeks of the pandemic than it did in the entire previous year. "They're giving up hope," Trotter says.[125]

"With teenagers, the symptoms of depression have been blurred by the pandemic," Lynn Zakeri says. "Teens are spending more time in their rooms for online schooling, and sometimes even their beds, as families juggle space issues. Add to that children and teenagers don't have the life experiences to put 2020 into perspective, so they might also struggle with hope for a better future."

Emergency-room visits involving children with mental-health issues have risen significantly since the pandemic began, according to an ABC Action News.com article. Dr. Jennifer Katzenstein, director of psychology and neuropsychology at Johns Hopkins All Children's Hospital, says in the article, "Throughout the pandemic for COVID-19, we've been very concerned about the mental health of our children, our adolescents, and our families. We've seen a number of children presenting with increased anxiety, increased difficulty separating from their parents or potentially returning to school, increasing signs of depression, increased suicidal ideation and also increased substance abuse and overdoses as well."[126]

Meanwhile, college students also struggled significantly with depression during the pandemic. Like children and teens, college students missed and mourned in-person time with their friends. The stress of remote learning negatively impacted them too. In addition, college students had their own distinctive challenges to overcome as the coronavirus upended the typical university experience by shutting down campuses and severely curtailing collegiate life.

In March 2020, nearly all campuses shut down, sending students home abruptly. As the University of Michigan blog puts it: "While many students may be happy to reconnect with family again, some have returned to abusive households, others to an empty fridge, and others to no home at all. Coursework was quickly transitioned to online for the remainder of the year. Much-anticipated culminating end of the year events, including commencement ceremonies, have been canceled. Many students have lost their on-campus or local jobs, and likewise, the job search for seniors has been severely disrupted. All the while, college students are experiencing these sudden and unexpected changes while physically separated from their familiar on-campus support systems."[127]

A survey of college students found many expressed concerns about depression and anxiety due to the pandemic. A survey of college students by Rise, a college affordability advocacy group, found that 75 percent of respondents dealt with higher levels of depression, stress and anxiety, and 52 percent had work hours slashed or were laid off from work. Overall, a mere 21 percent of those surveyed indicated "lives remained unchanged, other than classes being shifted online."[128]

The closure of college campuses has far-reaching effects. "College student hunger and homelessness, and the evictions and dropouts that will result from these closures, can have just as devastating of an impact," notes Max Lubin, CEO at Rise.[129]

Those high levels of depression and anxiety are just part of how hard the pandemic has hit college students. As BestColleges blog stated, "Forty-two percent of students said staying motivated to do well once courses moved online was a major problem for them." Falling academic grades also became a concern for them. Other concerns pointed out in the blog include "lost income from financial aid and on-campus work," "a digital opportunity gap" for low-income students, and punishment "for breaking COVID-19 social distancing rules."[130]

All sorts of factors have contributed to an increase of depression and other mental-health concerns among college students. College students especially are "prone to feelings of loneliness, and they experience higher rates of anxiety and depression compared to the general population," according to the University of Michigan's blog. With increased social isolation, more transitions, and uncertainty about the future, these feelings can worsen. "Removal from their social support system and extracurricular activities at their school can cause students to feel less connected with their friends, organizations, and hobbies. ... The situation they are living through is stressful and anxiety provoking, as there is a constant fear of the unknown in addition to a loss of control, making them especially vulnerable to developing mental health concerns."[131]

"The pandemic has been a hard time for young adults," Zakeri says. "Many of them had to end their college semesters early in 2020 and come home. Then they returned to school and many had to isolate in dorms or apartments while doing school online. It's been difficult for them to live with this whole sense of living on pause."

Getting off track can easily lead college students into depression. Michelle Maghami, a freshman at Pasadena City College in California, says that pre-pandemic, her schedule's structure kept her on track. A human biology major leaning towards dentistry, Maghami had to postpone her internships because of the pandemic, and lost income from her online shop. "It's easy to get depressed or feel like you're not being productive," she explains in a Los Angeles Times article. "You're kind of shut down in a way. That's the part I've been struggling the most with."[132]

Zakeri points out that parents have had to step up and pay closer attention to their children's mental health during the pandemic. "Parents have had to ensure that a melancholy mood isn't something more and that our kids are really doing okay because our whole gauge of normal behavior is sadder than it was pre-pandemic." She reminds parents to "never give up. Keep trying to communicate and connect with your kids, even if you feel like you're failing."

### Youth Depression Signs

Behaviors that may be signs of depression in young people mirror common signs of adult depression: Sad or irritable feelings, fatigue, and social isolation that persist for more than two weeks and interfere with a person's ability to function normally. But other potential signs of depression are distinctive symptoms found among young people.

Children who are depressed may show signs that include diminished performance in school, unsafe play behaviors (such as running into a street while playing), crying frequently, angry outbursts, problems sleeping or eating well, unexplained bodily complaints (like headaches that don't have a known physical cause), and persistent boredom, notes MedicineNet.com.[133] Additional signs of depression in children include talking about or acting on efforts to run away from home, and a loss of enjoyment in activities that a child had previously enjoyed, according to the American Academy of Child & Adolescent Psychiatry.[134]

Reimer also points to irritability and anger as depressive symptoms specifically in children and adolescents. "Parents usually think their teen is being moody, and can minimize the symptoms as being part of the normal teen's life," she says. "Parents can watch out for changes in routines or friends, isolating and spending too much time online or in their room, and alcohol or drug use."

Teens and young adults who are depressed also may exhibit such signs in addition to the classic symptoms of depression: Dropping grades at school, using or increasing use of alcohol and/or drugs, unhealthy eating or sleeping patterns, weight gain or loss, loneliness, and expressing hopelessness or a fixation on past failures, according to MentalHealthTreatment.net.[135] Other signs of depression in teens and young adults include driving recklessly and engaging in promiscuous or unprotected sex.[136]

For college students, depressive symptoms can masquerade as typical university life. "Watch out for sleeping in too much or insomnia in your student," cautions Dr. Lee. She also suggests asking questions like:

- Am I irritable because I'm stressed or starting to develop depression?
- Am I tearful because of the friend drama or legitimately depressed?
- Am I missing classes because I'm tired or because I can't sleep due to depression?

Zakeri emphasizes how important sleep is to a healthy mind and body. "Sleep is the number-one thing to staying healthy, so if you're not getting the right kind of sleep or sleeping too much that can create a pattern of unhealthy thoughts, which can exacerbate or lead to depression," she says.

The coronavirus pandemic also increased symptoms of stress and mental-health issues in younger children. HealthyChildren.org list the following as common indicators of stress and mental health problems for infants, toddlers, and young children:

- Backward progress in skills and developmental milestones
- Fussiness and irritability, startling and crying more easily, and more difficult to console
- Waking up more during the night
- Feeding issues such as frantic nippling, more reflux, constipation or loose stools, or new complaints of stomach pain
- Separation anxiety, seeming more clingy, withdrawn, or hesitant to explore
- Hitting, frustration, biting, and more frequent or intense tantrums
- Bedwetting after they're toilet trained
- Urgently expressed needs while seeming unable to feel satisfied[137]

HealthyChildren.org note that older children and teens who are stressed or dealing with mental-health problems may exhibit the following symptoms:

- Conflict and aggression or themes like illness or death during play
- Changes in mood that are not usual for your child, such as on-going irritability, feelings of hopelessness or rage, and frequent conflicts with friends and family
- Changes in behavior, such as stepping back from personal relationships
- A loss of interest in activities previously enjoyed
- A hard time falling or staying asleep, or starting to sleep all the time
- Changes in weight or eating patterns, such as never being hungry or eating all the time
- Problems with memory, thinking, or concentration
- Less interest in schoolwork and drop in academic effort
- Changes in appearance, such as lack of basic personal hygiene (within reason, since many are doing slightly less grooming during this time at home)
- An increase in risky or reckless behaviors, such as using drugs or alcohol
- Thoughts about death or suicide, or talking about it[138]

Concerned parents should start having conversations with their children about mental health. The HealthyChildren.org article recommends inviting "your child to talk about how they are feeling. Keep in mind that adolescents and young adults may try to hide their struggles because of fear, shame, or a sense of responsibility to avoid burdening others. Younger children may not know how to talk about these feelings but may show changes in their behavior or development."[139]

Parents who notice signs that their child has mental-health struggles should contact their pediatrician first, then if necessary reach out to a counselor for more help. The ABC Action News.com article also recommends that parents:

- Help children maintain good sleep schedules.
- Help children maintain some type of social connections.
- Find ways to reduce stress as a family.
- Sit down with kids and have open conversations about how they're feeling.[140]

Besides parents, others who are concerned about depressed children and teens can find ways to help them despite the pandemic. For example, schools and community organizations have been supporting students with telehealth sessions, virtual events, and socially distanced activities.[141]

**Youth Depression Treatment**

Depressed youth and their parents often turn to counseling therapy to treat the disease, sometimes combining therapy with prescription medication. "Comprehensive treatment often includes both individual and family therapy," says the American Academy of Child & Adolescent Psychiatry in Washington DC. For example, cognitive behavioral therapy (CBT) and interpersonal psychotherapy (IPT) are forms of individual therapy shown to be effective in treating depression. Treatment may also include the use of antidepressant medication.[142]

"What I find is a preference not to jump straight into medication, but to try talk therapy first, then consider medications if necessary," says counselor Reimer. "It's important to help youth and young adults to learn the skills to identify and self-manage their emotions."

The Mayo Clinic, headquartered in Rochester, Minneapolis, explains how therapy and medication may work to effectively treat depression in young patients: "Most children who take antidepressants for depression will improve with medication. However, combining medication with talk therapy (psychotherapy) is likely to be even more effective. Many types of psychotherapy may be helpful, but cognitive behavioral therapy and interpersonal therapy have been scientifically studied and shown to be effective for treating depression. … For some children and teenagers with mild symptoms, talk therapy alone may be beneficial."[143]

Cognitive behavioral therapy involves learning coping, communication, and problem-solving skills to manage emotions. Interpersonal therapy involves adapting to stress in relationships and building healthier relationships when possible.

For college students, universities have counseling centers that can assist with assessments of mental health, including depression, and can help guide students to qualified counselors and doctors. "I always encourage students to go to their school's counseling center for an assessment when they're unsure if it's sadness or depression they are experiencing," says Zakeri.

When youth take medication to treat depression, they are often prescribed smaller doses of antidepressants that adults take. Those antidepressant drugs include Escitalopram (Lexapro), Fluoxetine (Prozac), and Olanzapine and Fluoxetine (Symbyax), as well as their generic versions. [144]

Antidepressants often can successfully treat depression in young patients, but the drugs may sometimes raise the risk of suicide in developing brains. "Antidepressant drugs are often an effective way to treat depression and anxiety in children and teenagers. However, antidepressant use in children and teens must be monitored carefully, as rarely there can be severe side effects. Antidepressants carry a Food and Drug Administration (FDA) black box warning about a risk of increased suicidal thinking and behavior in some individuals under the age of 25."[145]

The Mayo Clinic advises parents and health-care professionals to monitor for any suicidal thoughts or behaviors when young people are transitioning on or off antidepressant drugs, stating: "The highest risk of suicidal thinking and behavior occurs during the first few months of treatment with an antidepressant [and] when the dosage is increased or decreased."[146]

## Early Intervention

Early intervention to help a young person with depression may prevent it from becoming more severe later in life. Researcher Elizabeth Miller, director of the division of adolescent medicine at Children's Hospital of Pittsburgh, says: "When you are seeing young people with symptoms consistent with depression it is really much, much better to get them connected to a pediatrician to get them a comprehensive mental health assessment and hook them into treatment sooner rather than later."[147] The American Academy of Child & Adolescent Psychiatry also urges that "early diagnosis and treatment are essential for depressed children."[148]

Another vital reason to treat depression in young people as soon as possible is because it may prevent associated problems from developing. As MedicineNet.com explains, "teens with depression are more likely to engage in self-mutilation. ... Adolescents with depression are also at risk of having poor school performance, early pregnancy, and engaging in alcohol and other drug abuse. As adults, people who suffered from depression during adolescence are at risk for job disruptions, as well as family and other social upheaval during adulthood."[149] Child Trends/DataBank Indicator says that "depression in adolescence is associated with higher levels of depression and poorer health outcome in young adulthood. Young adults who suffer from depression are more likely to have problems with psychological functioning, interpersonal relationships, employment, and substance abuse, and to be more dissatisfied with life. They also show higher rates of absenteeism from work."[150]

Suicide, which is linked to depression, is a leading cause of death among youth. The American Academy of Child & Adolescent Psychiatry in Washington DC warns that "depressed children and adolescents are at increased risk for committing suicide."[151] Clinical depression "is a leading cause of health impairment (morbidity) and death (mortality)," notes MedicineNet.com. "About three thousand adolescents and young adults die by suicide each year in the United States, making it the third leading cause of death in people [10 to 24] years of age."[152]

## A Parent's Perspective

It is difficult for parents to see their child suffer from depression and it can be hard to know how best to help. "Parents often feel helpless themselves," says Zakeri. "It's really hard to help someone who's hurting, but parents have to be the older/wiser grownup, to be the one to say, 'let's find out how we can get some help with this,' or 'let's look to other people to handle this.'"

Parents may initially respond with disbelief and denial, believing that depression is not a real disease and that if they minimize it, it will go away. "I tell parents that if your child had cancer, then you would immediately contact a medical professional and insist on treatment," says Reimer. "It should be the same with depression."

How can parents help? By talking to their child. "I recommend parents approach the topic in a safe, nonjudgmental way, with more empathy, by asking questions like, 'how are you doing?'" says Zakeri. "There are apps like iMood that can help people figure out what they're feeling, for example, much like the pain scale doctors and hospitals use."

When parents reach out to medical professionals for guidance or to make appointments for their offspring, "they should start with someone who specializes in mental health, like psychologists, psychiatrists, and licensed mental-health professionals," says Reimer.

Parents can encourage their college students to utilize the resources available on campus. "The college counseling center can determine if you have depression, give referrals for medical professionals, and provide other guidance to help the student improve their quality of life," says Dr. Lee. "However, it can be difficult for parents to recognize their limitations if an emerging adult doesn't want to seek help."

As we continue to remove barriers to treatment and the stigma surrounding mental illness, more youth struggling with depression will find hope. "Depression is a medical disease that's common and treatable," notes Reimer. "By giving parents and youth hope that this is a manageable situation, by empowering them to seek treatment, and by educating them about the disease, we can help more children, teens, and college students recover from depression and live full lives."

## Moving College Kids Forward

Despite the multiple challenges depressed college students face, there are ways for them to move into a more healthy future. The University of Michigan recommends these steps:

1. **Know that how you're feeling is okay.** Feeling sad, angry, anxious, and frustrated is normal during the pandemic. "You are allowed to feel this way and to communicate with others how you are feeling. It is also okay to sit with these emotions. If these feelings worsen to the extent that you are no longer able to function like your normal self, reach out to one of the resources listed below for additional support."[153] (See the Resources section for a list.)

2. **Stick with a routine.** Get out of bed at roughly the same time every day. Set mini-goals for classwork, such as one for each morning and afternoon. Eat three healthy meals each day, and work in at least one physical activity daily. "It is very good for your mental health to get some fresh air and go on a walk, run, or bike ride."[154]

3. **Maintain good sleep habits.** Try to get a consistent seven to nine hours of sleep per night. Stay off screens in the evening as you wind down, and stop drinking caffeine in the afternoon.

4. **Stay in touch with others.** We can feel lonely and removed from others during this time of social distancing, but make an effort to keep connected with others through regular video and phone calls with family and friends.

5. **Make time for yourself each day.** "Step away from the news and from your coursework to do something you enjoy and that you find relaxing or rejuvenating."[155]

PART I: THE DISEASE

# CHAPTER FIVE
## DEPRESSION'S IMPACT ON PATIENTS

**"Depression isn't about, 'Woe is me, my life is this, that, and the other;'
it's like having the worst flu all day that you just can't kick."**
—Robbie Williams, English singer-songwriter

What is depression? Doctors can give you a medical and biological analysis of what happens in your brain if you have depression, but for most people, that level of detail can be hard to follow. My first psychopharmacologist provided the following layman's description of depression that I've found to be very helpful in my understanding of the disease:

*What is happening in my brain? In your brain, you have brain cells. These cells are connected by synapses or pathways between cells. When you are depressed, these synapses or pathways are closed. The medication opens the pathways so your normal brain chemicals—the ones that make you feel good—can flow normally. The meds don't change who you are; rather, they let you be who you are.*

Today, technology has given us tools to diagnose depression. In August 2017, Google unveiled a new feature for U.S. users who search for "clinical depression" or "depression"—a short questionnaire they can take to test their levels of depression to assist in determining whether professional help is needed. "The clinically validated test, called PHQ-9, asks about energy, appetite, and concentration levels, among other things."[156]

Google developed the initiative with the National Alliance on Mental Illness (NAMI), and said it would not store responses to the questionnaire. "The results of the PHQ-9 can help you have a more informed conversation with your doctor," says Mary Giliberti, CEO of NAMI. "We hope that by making this information available on Google, more people will become aware of depression and seek treatment to recover and improve their quality of life."[157]

One of the challenges facing those with depression is finding the right medications and then dealing with any side effects of the prescribed medications. Another challenge is that what worked for one episode of depression may not be effective the next time or work in the same way. During my fourth bout of depression (18 years ago), my doctors prescribed the same medications that had brought me out of previous depressions, but those didn't work this time. The cycle of trying different combinations and dosages made the depression episode more prolonged and drawn out. My ruminations became even stranger, and my relationship with a woman with three children became unsustainable and ended abruptly.

By this point, I had been fighting depression for two years and wasn't in good shape at all. I was sorry the relationship ended, but I was very sick and needed to focus all my energy on getting better. Experts advise people who are depressed to not start a new relationship or make any major decisions.

Because depression is not viewed in the same vein as cancer or other diseases of the body, it can be difficult for those who suffer from it to have the support of their communities and families. If we could normalize depression even more, we could lower the rate of suicide and offer more hope to those who have the disease. We should be more willing to help the person during his or her depressive episodes, and understand that it's an illness and not fault the person for having this disease.

# CHAPTER SIX
## DEPRESSION'S IMPACT ON FAMILIES

**"Here is the tragedy: When you are the victim of depression, not only do you feel utterly helpless and abandoned by the world, you also know that very few people can understand, or even begin to believe, that life can be this painful."**
—Giles Andreae, English artist and poet

Those suffering from depression often face difficulties within their own families, because the disease is still so very misunderstood. Family members' reactions can help or hinder that person's treatment. Family members also are challenged when they know a person needs help, but are helpless to get him or her into treatment. Other times family members can grow weary of interacting with someone in the throes of a deep depression. Although it's never easy for the depressed person, it can be just as difficult for the family members of someone with depression.

My mother is a good example. Although she eventually realized that illness does run in our family, in the beginning she was in denial of her own depression, which first started after her parents died. Prior to that, my mom led a happy, fun life. Her depressions seemed to trigger when there was someone in the family dealing with health problems or a death in the immediate family. She didn't like doctors, so she wasn't helpful in seeking assistance for her depression. "We were watching it very closely because my grandmother had depression, my father had it, and others in the family did too," said my late mother, Dona Litzsinger.[158]

My father didn't understand the disease when I was younger either. He had difficulty dealing with my mother and the disease because they didn't really talk about it or tell us kids what was going on. It was one of those hidden things that no one talked about because no one knew exactly what it was. And my mother didn't always want the treatments available at the time because of various side effects. Society at that time viewed depression as a "mental breakdown" (a quite horrific term), and people didn't talk about it with extended family, much less friends or the public because of the stigma.

With depression, patients sometimes go years without a diagnosis, and often don't even realize this "blue feeling" has a potential cure. Sometimes the person doesn't want to admit they have or could have depression. I saw firsthand how that denial can impact a person as my mother didn't acknowledge her own depression diagnoses in the beginning. Of course, back then, we didn't have medication or treatments like we do now, but watching her suffer—even though I didn't know what to call it—made me determined to get help for my own depression.

That's a huge part of the disease—this hiding it, being afraid to talk about it while you're going through it because you don't think people will understand the illness. At the executive level, I've often thought there are probably a lot of executives who have some type of depression who can't talk about it—or think they can't talk about it. They're afraid that if they talk about it or acknowledge they are depressed, it may affect their career. I know I was concerned about that.

Dr. Norman Bengtsten was the first psychiatrist to diagnose my illness. Dr. Bengtsten and his wife were my grandparents' best friends, and we all called him Uncle Norman. I reached out to Norman when I didn't know what to do about how bad I was feeling mentally. He diagnosed me with depression within 15 minutes of our appointment, then told me that he had treated my grandfather, mother, and others in my mom's family. "The good thing was, unlike many people who were depressed in those days, Mark wanted to try to do something about it," remembers my father. "Mark was willing to learn about depression and not consider it some bad thing people were not willing to talk about."

## Depression on the Outside

For those close to someone with depression, deciphering which part of the person is the disease and which is his or her true self can be hard at times. Sometimes those with depression do a better job of hiding the disease behind a bubblier public persona. For example, my sister Robin, the second of our five siblings, was initially quite surprised to find out about my depression. "Mark was such a happy-go-lucky person, very sociable and involved in high school and college," she says. "I always looked up to him as my older brother and especially when boys came into the picture. He was a normal, happy, upper-middle-class, privileged-type person with no real problems."[159]

"The signs of depression were weird for Mark, and they didn't start out all at once but were gradual," adds my father. "During one of his major depression episodes, he was chairman of our company and things progressed where it was almost embarrassing because of Mark's lack of concentration and his serious issues with guilt—beyond what was normal—and that rendered him unable to let go of and move on from specific incidents."

My younger sister, Heidi Baumann, the third child in our family, wasn't surprised by my depression diagnosis because of our mother's illness. "I think my mother and her depression issues were really hard on Mark because of him being the oldest," says Heidi.[160]

Shawn Stratman, the fourth sibling, says she always knew when I was struggling with depression. "He would ruminate and ask a lot of questions, the same questions over and over again. I'd talk to him about it, but he would go back to the same thing over and over," Shawn notes. "But, of course, it was something [helping him] I needed and wanted to do because he's my brother."[161]

With eight years between Shawn and myself, she and I didn't become very close until some of my later depressive episodes. "That's when our relationship really grew—when I was a grown woman and he was battling this," she recalls. "Mark could hide his depression during an episode for short periods of time. He could pull himself together, but it would be a struggle."

My brother, Todd Litzsinger, the youngest in our family, had a different experience, partly because of our 10-year age difference. "Mark in his depression would describe things over and over, even minor issues that he couldn't let go," says Todd, adding that he idolized me as his older brother. "He's a very truthful and honest person, but the depression made him increasingly paranoid and overly concerned about doing right and avoiding wrong."[162]

### Knowledge Is Understanding

My own family's reactions and interactions during my depression episodes underscored to me the importance of family members' understanding the disease as much as possible in order to support their loved ones during their journey out of depression. Here are some things families should be aware of when a member has been diagnosed with depression:

- **Risk factor.** "Family members should know a couple of things when someone in their family has been diagnosed with depression," says Dr. William Scheftner. "The number one is that they too are at risk for depression, because if you have one member of the family with depression, your chances of identifying another member of the family with depression probably doubles."
- **Expectations.** Everyone reacts to depression treatment differently—what works for one person might not work for another. Family members need to be aware of that and adjust their expectations accordingly. "Part of that adjustment is the fact that someone being treated for depression will still have bad days," explains Dr. Mark Pollack,[163] former chairman of the Department of Psychiatry at Rush University Medical Center in Chicago, Illinois. Sometimes people expect the treatment to kick in right away, but that doesn't usually happen. Medications can take weeks to show results. (See Chapter 22 for more on what family members should know about depression treatment.)

- **Compassion.** When a person goes through depression, they can be in a fog at times, even when getting treatment. "My sister Heidi and I helped Mark during his last major depression. We went with him to ECT [electroconvulsive or shock therapy] treatments and brought him home afterwards to make sure he got sleep, ate, etc. It was eye-opening as a sibling to watch what happened to him," says Robin.

- **Patience.** For some with depression, recovery can take years, which can really wear on family members. Other times, the particular manifestation of the depression can stretch their limits. "For me, it was Mark's obsessive-compulsive disorder and ruminating. It was hard to hear the same thing over and over and over, day after day without any change," says Robin. "No matter how many times you told Mark to move past it, he couldn't get beyond it. It was really hard." During those periods, she stresses how important it was for her to recognize it was the disease talking and not her brother.

- **Support.** It's important for all family members to be as supportive as they can during the patient's treatment and recovery. That helps to provide the patient with the foundation on which to build his or her recovery. The support can be as low-key as phone calls to check in with the patient or as hands-on as driving the person to treatment and bringing him or her home afterwards. "Depression treatment is time-consuming and frustrating because it can go on and on and on," says my father. "That's why family support is so critical to the patient."

Support also can come in the form of helping the person cope at work while battling depression. Todd worked with me at our family company during my worst depression, which started when I was 47 and lasted two years. "Mark would get on these tangents over things that weren't as big as he was making them out to be, and it became very clear that something was wrong," notes Todd. "He really went into this depression where I and my cousin at work tried to keep things going, to distract everybody else to prevent people from noticing certain things about Mark's behavior."

- **Professional help.** Encourage your family member to get help through the best medical care available. I highly recommend seeking psychiatric care at a teaching hospital if possible. "You need to get them to a professional who can analyze and start the process. That's the first thing they should do. Don't wait around for it to cure itself, because it could get worse," says my father.

## A Changing World?
We hope that the world is changing, that depression won't be as stigmatized or marginalized as it has been in the past. Having family members who understand depression is essential to recovery. "You have to both understand what depression is and that there are ways to get professional help, that there can be a light at the end of the tunnel," notes my father.

Part of the problem with depression is that we use the term generically. There are actually two types of depression: situational depression and genetic depression. Depression is like a final common pathway that patients can develop as a result of genetic or other biologic vulnerabilities, life events and stressors, cognitive style or some combination of those. With genetic depression, a person is genetically predisposed to have a chemical imbalance. "When you really wrap your mind around that, my desire is that we would address it as genetic depression, which would be what Mark and our family carry—a true genetic disease—and situational depression, which is incidental, onset depression where something happens, and your body and mind respond with depression," says Shawn. "Ironically, Mark is the most generous person I know. He sees a problem someone may be having and dives in to help fix it. All of that part of the person is cloaked during a depressive episode." She stresses that making this distinction will help family members assist their loved one through the depression with more compassion and understanding.

Families play a large part in a person's recovery from depression. "I don't think anyone can come out of depression without someone helping them," said my mother. My father adds, "I think Mark's recovery has been so remarkable because of the huge role his siblings played in helping him. They are all super kids and really care about each other. They all came together and did what they could to be supportive of Mark, more than he probably realized."

PART I: THE DISEASE

# CHAPTER SEVEN
## DEPRESSION AND LONELINESS

**"Try to understand the blackness, lethargy, hopelessness, and loneliness they're going through. Be there for them when they come through the other side. It's hard to be a friend to someone who's depressed, but it is one of the kindest, noblest, and best things you will ever do."**
—Stephen Fry, English actor, comedian and writer

The correlation between loneliness and depression is strong, and both conditions are on the rise. During the social distancing of the coronavirus pandemic, loneliness increased at alarming rates. People can be alone without feeling lonely, but too much solitude—a lack of regular in-person contact with other human beings—can often lead to loneliness. People experience loneliness when they have a negative emotional response to perceived isolation. Loneliness can harm mental health in a variety of ways, including promoting depression.

"We are biologically wired to connect with others, and when we are disconnected, our neurocircuitry crashes. In other words, we experience cognitive decline, get anxious and depressed, and may find ourselves self-medicating with substances," says Liza R Clancy, LCSW, a doctor of behavioral health at Seasons Psychotherapy & Wellness in Bradley Beach, New Jersey.[164]

Loneliness can both contribute to people developing depression and exacerbate existing depression. Beyond that, loneliness is linked to a variety of other conditions that have a correlation with depression. "Feeling lonely correlates with mental-health distress, including anxiety and depression," said Dr. Dara Schwartz, a clinical psychologist with Sharp Mesa Vista Hospital in San Diego, California. "In addition to mental-health concerns, loneliness has been linked to heart problems, diabetes, stroke, memory complaints, drug-abuse risk and elevated blood pressure."[165]

According to the mental-health website Verywellmind.com[166], loneliness can negatively impact people's mental and physical health in a diverse variety of ways, including:

- Alcoholism and drug use
- Altered brain function
- Alzheimer's disease progression
- Antisocial behavior
- Cardiovascular disease and stroke
- Decreased memory and learning
- Depression and suicide
- Increased stress levels
- Poor decision-making

Depression is a complex condition that people may suffer from regardless of whether or not they're lonely, but "[s]till, feelings of social isolation or dissatisfaction with your relationships can absolutely play a part," according to *Healthline.com.*[167] "Prolonged loneliness can affect mental health. ... It can make any symptoms you're already dealing with worse, for one. But it can also factor into the development of serious mental health conditions, including depression."[168]

"Although the symptoms associated with loneliness and depression are very similar, it is difficult to solidify a link," says Dr. Bryan Bruno, medical director of New York City-based Mid City TMS, which specializes in treating depression. "When someone is depressed, they may be restless, but lethargic, and moody with appetite and sleep changes. The same is apparent for people who express feeling lonely. Often, loneliness can trigger depression or vice versa."[169]

The 2018 United Kingdom research study entitled "Self-Disgust as a Potential Mechanism Explaining the Association Between Loneliness and Depression" explored the how a feeling of self-disgust impacts loneliness and depressive symptoms.[170]

How does that connection play out? According to Healthline.com, "[s]elf-disgust—which often relates to low self-worth—might involve negative feelings or harsh judgment toward specific actions or yourself as a whole. … If you fixate on these thoughts and believe you don't deserve love or friendship, you might act in ways that reinforce this belief. You might, for example, turn down invitations, telling yourself, 'They don't really want to see me.' When you do see others, you might constantly worry about how they really feel toward you. This can greatly diminish the value of your interactions, leaving you feeling isolated and miserable—even among people you care about. The end result is often a cycle of distress that reinforces loneliness. Eventually, you might begin to see yourself as hopeless and believe there's nothing you can do to improve the situation."[171] That state of mind can promote depression.

**Loneliness Pre-Pandemic**

Loneliness was already a significant mental-health issue prior to the COVID-19 pandemic. In 2019, before the pandemic began, more than half of all Americans surveyed by the health-insurer Cigna reported feeling lonely: 63 percent of men and 58 percent of women.[172] Another major pre-pandemic study from the Kaiser Family Foundation in 2018 found a lower yet still significant number of Americans—22 percent—said they experienced loneliness.[173]

"People who experience loneliness express negative emotions when engaging with people, like rejection and anticipating poor social interactions. People also cite sadness as the cause of not engaging and withdrawing from others, bringing about loneliness. While being alone is not the same as feeling lonely, solitude can trigger negative thoughts, which activate negative emotions," explains Dr. Bruno.

Studies show that the absence of human connection actually impacts mortality by increasing your chances of dying prematurely by 26 percent—enough to rival smoking more than 15 packs of cigarettes a day, according to Dr. Bruno. "There is also evidence that loneliness can affect your overall health more so than your eating habits or environmental pollution," he says. "Socialization and having positive interactions can also serve as distractions from negative thoughts stemming from depression. It seems as though these two states of being go hand in hand, and it is impossible to decipher which comes first—depression or loneliness."

Former U.S. Surgeon General Dr. Vivek H. Murthy pointed out in a CNN.com article that loneliness is a substantial and growing health problem. "Loneliness is an important health priority. There's growing evidence that we have a strong association between loneliness and concerning health outcomes."[174]

Even before the pandemic, loneliness impacted our health. As *The Wall Street Journal* noted in April 2020, "[e]vidence shows that social interaction is a biological requirement, much like eating, drinking, and sleeping. Our ability to learn to talk, play, acquire new skills, fall in love, conduct business, and age in good health all hinge on our motivation to connect with other people, social neuroscientists have found. ... Even before Covid-19 forced us to self-isolate, a quarter of Americans were chronically lonely—a psychological state that is invisible, contagious and physically damaging, much like the virus itself."[175]

### Loneliness During the Pandemic

Once COVID-19 spread around the world and health officials declared it a pandemic, cases of both viral infections and loneliness increased. People faced a challenging dilemma. They learned a key way to prevent the new coronavirus from spreading was by "social distancing," which translated into staying away from others as much as possible. Lockdowns and quarantines began across the world to help stop the virus from running rampant. Many people got together virtually rather than in person, and those who did see others physically aimed to stay at least six feet apart. Although social distancing helped physical health, there was a mental-health cost as people's loneliness grew.

Shortly after the pandemic began in March 2020, people of all demographic backgrounds reported feeling even lonelier than usual. "Since lockdowns and stay-at-home orders were instated, roughly a third of American adults report feeling lonelier than usual, according to an April 2020 survey by social-advice company SocialPro. Another survey, also conducted in April 2020, for financial research group ValuePenguin, put the number even higher at 47 percent. If the stereotype of a lonely person is a frail, elderly adult who lives alone, the coronavirus pandemic has exposed the truth that was there all along: anyone, anywhere, of any age can experience loneliness."[176]

"The pandemic has forced us to isolate so on top of fearing for our lives, we have lost our support systems and the comfort of our routines," says Liza Clancy. Soon after the pandemic started, most Americans reported feeling lonely at least sometimes: 76 percent of men and 75 percent of women. Many Americans said the pandemic made them feel lonely constantly ("always or often"): 31 percent of men and 26 percent of women.[177]

The age group most likely to report experiencing loneliness was teens and young adults. Seventy-five percent of those between the ages of 18 and 23 said they felt lonely because of the pandemic, while 80 percent of those between the ages of 24 and 39 reported a similar feeling.[178] The impact of the pandemic on young people's mental health was "alarming," a MedicalNewsToday.com article declared. Results of a study of people between the ages of 18 and 35 showed that "[r]oughly 65% of study participants reported increased feelings of loneliness since the declaration of COVID-19 as a pandemic" and "80 percent of participants reported 'significant depressive symptoms' during the pandemic."[179]

Young people reached out to each other online while physically apart, however, those connections don't seem to have ease their loneliness, and may have actually made them feel even lonelier. Girls spent more time on social media and boys spent more time playing video games than they did prior to the pandemic, according to *The Wall Street Journal*. Yet, they still reported feeling lonely. The "reasons underlying the increased loneliness" include "spending more time online and less time in person with friends."[180]

Many older adults also said the pandemic made them feel lonely. Sixty-seven percent of people between the ages of 40 and 54 reported feeling lonely during the pandemic, while 72 percent of those age 55 and older said the same.[181] As *The Wall Street Journal* pointed out, older adults, who are more vulnerable to coronavirus than most younger adults, tend to be more socially isolated than younger people. "The combination of social isolation and loneliness is very unhealthy for anyone, but for older adults, it's particularly bad," said Bert Uchino, a University of Utah psychology professor who studies the ways in which social relationships affect health. "Just about every biological system is impacted in one way or another by psychosocial relationships."[182]

Although online socializing made younger adults feel lonelier, it seemed to help older adults feel less lonely. A Time.com article explains that "research suggests not everyone benefits equally from digital interactions. Several studies have found that tools like video chats and instant messages may help elderly adults feel less lonely, especially if they're physically isolated from others and cannot otherwise socialize. But, interestingly, research shows that loneliness may subside for younger adults when they reduce their social media usage. In regular life, that may be because endless scrolling through other people's social-media posts makes young people feel left out, or it may be because it's replacing valuable in-person moments."[183]

Compounding the widespread loneliness during the pandemic was that many people felt they didn't have anyone to talk to about their personal problems. "Loneliness hurts. Most of us have experienced this," an article from the Greater Good Science Center explains. "Especially in this time of quarantine, many can feel lonely. With the advent of technology and social media and the ever-increasing speed of life, we may feel more connected in some ways, but, on the other hand, 'human moments' of actual face-to-face exchange without interruption can become rarer. A sociological study shows that disconnect seems to be on the rise, with one out of four Americans feeling like they have no one to talk to about personal problems. Loneliness is the leading reason people seek out therapy."[184]

Previously, Americans may have found it tough to talk about their loneliness because of feeling ashamed about it. However, the pandemic has stripped away some of the stigma of loneliness, making it more acceptable for people to discuss those feelings. "We are all going through this life-altering ordeal, and our lives have all been turned upside-down," Dr. Murthy says in a CNN.com article. "Most people recognize it. Many people are, in fact, struggling. ... When we recognize that we, and everyone, are vulnerable, it can make it easier to reach out, to check in with someone, to be honest about how you're doing as well."[185]

The common problem of loneliness during the pandemic also appears to fuel depression. "Studies have found a link between social isolation and depression," an article from *The Wall Street Journal* declares. "And the uncertainty can fuel the feelings of hopelessness and helplessness that are a hallmark of depression."[186]

### Ways to Relieve Loneliness

When people feel lonely, it's how they deal with those feelings that makes the difference in whether or not their loneliness also makes them feel depressed. For those who have loved ones they think might be lonely, Liza Clancy recommends finding common interests, such as a TV show, podcast series, or book, as a point of connection. "Not only is this a reference point for discussion, but the lonely individual may take some comfort in knowing that he or she is not alone in watching the show," she says.

Another tangible way to help alleviate loneliness in family members or friends is to initiate routine contact at specific times of day, like an appointment. "This not only serves as a check-in and a regular time to connect but gives the lonely individual something to look forward to," Clancy says.

Here are 11 ways for individuals to respond to loneliness that may help prevent it from leading to—or exacerbating—depression.

1. **Regulate emotions.** Emotional control is the key to stop lonely feelings from turning into an attitude of self-disgust. "The

researchers who explored the association between loneliness and depression suggest that reframing or suppressing (pushing away) unwanted thoughts can help reduce their impact and prevent the negative thought cycles that often trigger feelings of depression," a Healthline.com article explains. "So, when a friend doesn't pick up the phone, try reframing, 'They don't want to talk to me' to, 'They're probably busy, so I'll try again later.' If no one seems available, you might start to feel a little unwanted. But instead of letting these thoughts take over, try distracting yourself by thinking about something else or spending time on something that makes you happy."[187]

2.   **Practice mindfulness meditation.** Being fully present with the experience of loneliness can help build resilience that strengthens people to endure it. One way people can reframe their thoughts when they feel lonely is to practice mindfulness. A Healthline.com article suggests mindful acceptance to "get more comfortable with distressing thoughts" and points out that "[m]indfulness helps you learn to accept these thoughts and then let them go before they affect your perception of yourself."[188] A Greater Good Science Center article notes that people should "[s]imply be with the sensations, thoughts, and emotions that arise without trying to control or change them. Observe them with the kindness of a mother watching her child at play. Be patient. If the emotions get uncomfortable, muster up your valor, strength, tenacity, and patience. Set yourself a time limit and do not get up until the time is over. You can start with five minutes and eventually work up to sitting for 20 or 30 minutes at a time."[189]

3.   **Limit screen time.** Getting a break from staring at screens can help people rejuvenate in ways that ease loneliness, according to a Mayo Clinic article that advises turning "off electronic devices for some time each day, including 30 minutes before bedtime.

Make a conscious effort to spend less time in front of a screen—television, tablet, computer and phone."[190]

4. **Connect with nature.** Enjoying time outdoors in natural settings can enlarge people's perspectives so they feel less lonely. "If connecting with people is a challenge, connect with nature," a Greater Good Science Center article recommends. "[T]aking walks in nature can increase our well-being, even in the case of depression. … [E]xposure to nature increases our sense of connectedness and closeness and even makes us more caring and ready to share with others. Connecting with nature can help broaden that vision and inspire an experience of awe at the view of a landscape. Cultivating awe through nature can also help broaden our perspective."[191]

5. **Take good care of the body.** Mental health can improve when physical health does. A Greater Good Science Center article notes that "[a]s part of our distracted lifestyle, we often don't listen to our body. We eat the wrong foods, drink, stay up too late, and forget to exercise or over-exercise. We also carry around the false notion that our body's well-being is independent from that of our mind. This is not the case. As anyone who has started a healthy diet or exercise regimen knows, when we start to take care of our body, we naturally feel better and, with a positive state of mind, our whole outlook on life changes."[192]

6. **Maintain a regular daily routine.** Keeping a regular schedule is important to people's mental health, according to a Mayo Clinic article. "In addition to sticking to a regular bedtime routine, keep consistent times for meals, bathing and getting dressed, work or study schedules, and exercise. Also set aside time for activities you enjoy. This predictability can make you feel more in control."[193]

7.  **Set priorities.** People can avoid unnecessary stress by setting priorities for how to best use their limited time and energy. "Don't become overwhelmed by creating a life-changing list of things to achieve while you're home. ... Set reasonable goals each day and outline steps you can take to reach those goals. Give yourself credit for every step in the right direction, no matter how small. And recognize that some days will be better than others."[194]

8.  **Focus on positive thoughts and find spiritual strength.** Positive thinking and faith can help people overcome loneliness. "Choose to focus on the positive things in your life, instead of dwelling on how bad you feel. ... Consider starting each day by listing things you are thankful for. Maintain a sense of hope, work to accept changes as they occur and try to keep problems in perspective. If you draw strength from a belief system, it can bring you comfort during difficult times."[195]

9.  **Serve others in need.** Focusing on service to others helps lonely people feel more connected and appreciated. "There is always someone suffering more than we are. ... This gives us the opportunity to approach others with kindness and a sense of service. No matter what our capabilities, we can always contribute to others with as little as a smile or more."[196] Even during the pandemic, volunteer opportunities abound. "Research shows that compassion and service can be of tremendous benefit. ... Helping others can immediately change our perspective and re-energize us, which is why compassion has been linked to well-being."[197]

"Alleviating loneliness is about increasing connection and making meaning," Clancy says. "One way to make an inroad is to reduce the focus on oneself by performing a charitable act. Thinking of and doing for others provides meaning and restores self-worth."

10. **Ask for help.** People who are struggling with loneliness and/or depression should reach out for the help they need without hesitation. Here are five tips from a Mayo Clinic.org article to guide you to the help you need:

- Call or use social media to contact a close friend or loved one—even though it may be hard to talk about your feelings.
- Contact a minister, spiritual leader, or someone in your faith community.
- Contact your employee-assistance program, if your employer has one, and get counseling or ask for a referral to a mental-health professional.
- Call your primary-care provider or mental-health professional to ask about appointment options to talk about your anxiety or depression and get advice and guidance. Some may provide the option of phone, video, or online appointments.
- Contact organizations such as the National Alliance on Mental Illness (NAMI) or the Substance Abuse and Mental Health Services Administration (SAMHSA) for help and guidance.
  If you're feeling suicidal or thinking of hurting yourself, seek help. Contact your primary-care provider or a mental-health professional. Or call a suicide hotline. In the U.S., call the National Suicide Prevention Lifeline at 1-800-273-TALK (1-800-273-8255) or use its webchat at suicidepreventionlifeline.org/chat.[198]

11. **Empower yourself.** Give yourself permission to make changes, both big and small, to help alleviate feeling lonely. "When people who suffer from loneliness, depression, and addiction are stakeholders in their well-being, we see improvement in not only their mental health, but their physical condition as well," Clancy says.

Unfortunately, both loneliness and depression are on the rise across the world today, and these conditions often feed off each other. However, the good news is that both conditions can be treated together. People can overcome loneliness and relieve depression by intentionally doing what they can to live a healthy lifestyle by asking for help from professionals and friends and family.

# CHAPTER EIGHT
## DEPRESSION AND TECHNOLOGY

**"It's so difficult to describe depression to someone who's never been there, because it's not sadness. I know sadness. Sadness is to cry and to feel. But it's that cold absence of feeling—that really hollowed-out feeling."**
—J.K. Rowling, British author of the Harry Potter series

People use technology to stay connected to the outside world in vital ways, from learning the latest news to exchanging messages with friends and family. Personal computers and mobile devices such as smartphones have become an important part of daily life, especially during the pandemic, which has forced many people to work, go to school, and interact with others remotely. For those experiencing depression, technology like mental-health apps and video conferencing can even boost their well-being.

However, technology does have its downside. It doesn't offer the same type of connection that in-person contact does, and technology itself can be addictive. When people become addicted to technology or use technology to withdraw from the world, it can lead them to struggle with depression.

Technology addiction is a growing problem for those of all ages. Although people speak anecdotally about technology addiction, it hasn't yet been classified by psychiatrists as an official condition. Still, it remains a serious issue. Those who are addicted to (or overuse) technology spend hours each day scrolling through Internet content such as emails, videos, articles, and social-media posts. In the process, they may encounter negative content and online comments that can exacerbate depression. They also may lose time for well-being activities that can help relieve depression, like sleeping, exercising, and visiting friends in person.

"Research has revealed that over-dependence on technology directly impacts depression, anxiety, stress, self-esteem, loneliness, and feelings of rejection in families, and has negative health implications, such as addiction," says Dr. Arayeh Norouzi, a rapid transformational coach in Pacific Grove, California. "Some findings showed a positive correlation between social-media addiction and depression, and revealed that depression significantly predicted social-media addition."[199]

According to research by the National Institutes of Health, "Depression is the most frequently reported psychiatric symptom associated with Internet overuse."[200] The study also notes that "Internet addiction is a psychosocial disorder and its characteristics are as follows: tolerance, withdrawal symptoms, affective disorders, and problems in social relations. Internet usage creates psychological, social, school and/ or work difficulties in a person's life. ... Excessive Internet use may create a heightened level of psychological arousal, resulting in little sleep, failure to eat for long periods, and limited physical activity, possibly leading to the user experiencing physical and mental health problems such as depression, OCD, low family relationships and anxiety."[201]

Another study published in *CyberPsychology & Behavior*, reports its "findings suggest that increased levels of depression are associated with those who become addicted to the Internet. This suggests that clinical depression is significantly associated with increased levels of personal Internet use."[202]

How much Internet use is considered excessive? And what amount of time online constitutes addiction? The *CyberPsychology & Behavior* study explains: "Addicts in this study used the Internet an average of 38 hours per week for nonacademic or nonemployment purposes, which caused detrimental effects such as poor grade performance among students, discord among couples, and reduced work performance among employees. This is compared to nonaddicts who used the Internet an average of 8 hours per week with no significant consequences reported."[203]

It is important to consider the way people interact with technology when determining whether or not they're addicted. According to Dr. Kimberly Young in HealthyPlace.com, there are eight criteria to diagnose Internet addiction:

1. Preoccupation with the Internet, including thinking about previous online interactions and anticipating the upcoming online session.
2. Needing increasingly more time online to achieve the same level of satisfaction.
3. Repeated unsuccessful attempts to curb or halt Internet usage.
4. Trying to curtail Internet usage engenders a feeling of restlessness, irritability, moodiness, or depression.
5. Frequently staying online for longer than intended.
6. Losing or jeopardizing significant relationships, career or educational opportunities because of the Internet.
7. Lying to family members, friends, therapists, and others to hide Internet involvement.
8. Using the Internet to escape everyday problems or to relieve feelings of anxiety, guilt, depression, or helplessness.

If any of these statements resonates with you, you may suffer from an addiction to the Internet.[204]

After the coronavirus pandemic began in early 2020, many people spent even more time online than they had previously. Work, school, and socializing often took place online rather than in person during the pandemic. Technology became a lifeline for people to interact with others in ways that didn't threaten their physical health.

"Research shows that Internet use is used as a coping strategy, and is considerably increased in crisis, such as the COVID-19 pandemic," Dr. Arayeh Norouzi says. "During the 2020 COVID-19 pandemic, many researchers have found a significant increase in digital technology overuse in both adolescents and children."

Although technology can help some people stay connected when in-person meetings aren't possible, experts and health professionals express concerns about increase in technology usage and its links to depression. "Technology addiction is more widespread than you may think. According to a study published by the International Journal of Neuropsychiatric Medicine, one in eight Americans suffer from a form of problematic use of the internet, what's more, these rates being as high as 30% in some countries around the world."[205]

Technology addiction and depression can have a symbiotic relationship. What exactly is the association between the two conditions? "Addiction to tech likely stems from a combination of biological, genetic, and environmental factors. People who are dependent on technology are more likely to have preexisting mental health conditions like depression, anxiety, social phobias, and sleep disorders. People prone to low self-esteem or those who deal with a lot of stress at work and home are more likely to develop compulsive technology behaviors. There are warning signs to look out for if you are worried about technology addiction. Some of these include a sense of euphoria while plugged in, feeling anxious, ashamed, guilty, or depressed as a result of technology use, skipping on sleep, and dishonesty about technology use. There are even some physical signs to look out for, like sudden weight gain or loss, carpal tunnel syndrome, headaches, and neck or backaches."[206]

**Technology and Children**
Studies show how people of all ages experience technology addiction and depression. Even children may struggle with technology overuse and depression. Parents may debate whether or not children can actually become addicted to technology, but many are seriously concerned about how much their children are using technology, and how those habits are affecting their mental health.

"Digital screening acts similar to narcotics in the brain," Norouzi explains. "Digital devices are intentionally designed to keep us hooked.

With every swipe, alert, text, or image, we get a surge of dopamine. These chemicals change our brain, training us to need more dopamine hits from the devices and traps us in a feedback loop that is impossible to resist."

According to the Child Mind Institute in New York, "Whatever you call it, a lot of parents are expressing worries that their children are addicted to their devices. Is the behavior that parents are concerned about really addiction? What parents are alarmed about is usually two things: the sheer amount of time their kids spend on screens, and their kids' resistance to cutting back on that screen time. Getting them to put away their devices and come to dinner, engage in other activities, go outside or do their homework (without also checking social media and streaming TV shows) seems to be an increasingly uphill battle."[207]

Children who use technology too much or in unhealthy ways may be at increased their risk of depression. "While experts say that parents should remain skeptical of the notion of addiction, they also argue that parents should be alert for potential negative fallout from screen use. Apps and games are designed to keep us engaged as much as possible, and it can be hard for children to exercise self-control when their impulse is to keep scrolling. There is ample evidence that intense social media use is correlated with an increase in anxiety and depression as teenagers, especially girls, compare themselves unfavorably to their peers and worry about missing out. Research shows that excessive gaming—spending two-thirds or more of free time—is correlated with negative mental health outcomes, including higher incidence of anxiety, depression and substance use."[208]

How much time are children spending online, and what content are they interacting with the most? According to a report by Common Sense Media, headquartered in San Francisco, California, "On average, children from birth to age 8 use about two and a half hours (2:24) of screen media a day. Online videos now dominate children's screen time."[209]

There are mental-health factors to consider when reflecting on how children are using technology since the pandemic. "The amount of time children spend watching online videos had already doubled over the past few years. What might this mean in terms of the types of content they are exposed to, or their interactions with others online, especially if they are spending even more time in these activities now that they are stuck at home more often?"[210]

Also, the Common Sense Media report points out that pre-pandemic, children in the five to eight age group had begun using "connected" media applications, like social gaming, more often. "Many of these games and apps mean that children are interacting with other users online in ways parents may not always be aware of. Given that this practice had already started as a mode of entertainment among this age group before the virus exploded, what might this mean for children whose only form of 'play' may now be online, without the supervision of teachers, playground monitors, or even parents? Will their interactions with other gamers online lead to more cyberbullying and other negative experiences, or to a greater sense of social connection and new friendships?"[211]

Dr. Norouzi notes that "the root of addiction is the lack of connection. When we cannot fill our inner void with positive activities, interactions, thoughts, and sensations, we resort to filling it with negative activities and addictive or numbing behaviors, such as alcohol, drugs, shopaholism [addiction to shopping], workaholism [addiction to work], and digital screening. When we retrieve the digital devices from our children, it's essential to replace them with a good dose of connection and high-quality activities to decrease the withdrawal symptoms."

Children's use of social media is another factor that may affect their mental health. As Dr. Rangan Chatterjee says in a BBC News article, "Social media is having a negative impact on mental health. I do think it is a big problem and that we need some rules. How do we educate society to use technology so it helps us rather than harms us?"[212] The BBC News article lists the following suggestions for how parents can help children use technology wisely:

- Keep an eye on how much time children spend online and ensure it is not interfering with activities such as socializing, exercising, eating, and sleeping.
- Consider bans on devices at mealtimes and take them away an

hour before bedtime. Do not let children charge devices in their rooms.

- Talk regularly to children about what they do online, what posts they have made that day, who they are friends with and how it is affecting their mood.
- With younger children, have access to passwords to regularly check content.
- Remember, Facebook, Twitter, and Instagram officially bar children under 13 from having accounts.
- Encourage children to use the Internet for creative things—helping with homework, making their own content.[213]

## Technology and Teens

Teens tend to use technology even more than children do. The evidence connecting heavy or unhealthy technology use and depression is significant for this age group. "Teens who spend far too much time on the Internet run the risk of developing depression," warns a *HealthDay News* article.[214] That article cites an Australian research study of teens: "The risk of becoming depressed was 2.5 times higher among teens who were addicted to the Internet compared with those who weren't."[215] Lead researcher Lawrence T. Lam from the School of Medicine, Sydney, and the University of Notre Dame Australia says of the study's findings: "Given the results obtained from the study, even mentally healthy young people may succumb to depression after a long exposure of problematic use of the Internet. The mental health consequences of problematic Internet use for those who have already had a history of psychological or psychiatric problems would be more damaging. ... This study has a direct implication on the prevention of mental illness among young people. The results of the study indicated that young people who use the Internet pathologically are most at risk of mental problems and would develop depression when they continue with that behavior. ... Screening for at-risk individuals in the school setting could be considered as an effective early prevention strategy."[216]

Among teens, smartphone and social-media use are the most

common concerns associated with technology addiction and depression. The more teens use smartphones, the higher their depression and suicide risks become, according to a research study from California's San Diego State University.[217] The research "found that teens who spend five or more hours per day on their devices are 71 percent more likely to have one risk factor for suicide. And that's regardless of the content consumed. Whether teens are watching cat videos or looking at something more serious, the amount of screen time—not the specific content—goes hand in hand with the higher instances of depression."[218]

According to Jean Twenge, a psychologist and one of the study's authors, "It's an excessive amount of time spent on the device. So half an hour, an hour a day, that seemed to be the sweet spot for teen mental health in terms of electronic devices. At two hours a day there was only a slightly elevated risk. And then three hours a day and beyond is where you saw the more pronounced increase in those who had at least one suicide risk factor. ... I think a great rule for both teens and adults is to try to keep your use at two hours a day or less. And then you put that phone down, and you spend the rest of your time on things that are better for mental health and happiness, like sleeping, seeing friends and family face to face, getting out and exercising. These are all things that are linked to better mental health."[219]

Despite the concerns of spending too much time on smartphones, teens may be able to use smartphone apps to help treat depression. Some health apps can help lower depressive symptoms, according to research published in the journal *World Psychiatry*. A study of volunteers suffering from various mental-health conditions, including anxiety, bipolar disorder, and depression, tracked participants' use of mental-health apps. Researchers found that "while all the apps were effective in reducing symptoms, those apps that were self-contained and did not incorporate clinician feedback were more effective than those that relied on clinicians. Apps and other digital services ... can be a complement [to medical services]. The bottom line: Technology, in the form of apps for depression and anxiety, may be a good antidote for some of the problems created by that very same technology."[220]

Heavy social-media use may play a key role to depression especially in teen girls. "Screen time, and more recently social media use, has been repeatedly identified as a potential cause of adolescents' worsening mental health symptoms. This claim is uncertain, but recent meta-analyses and narrative reviews reveal a mix of small positive, negative, and mostly neutral correlations between both screen time and social media use and adolescents' mental health. ... Social media emerges as a correlate of worse mental health more frequently among adolescent girls, but the direction of influence is uncertain."[221]

The coronavirus pandemic, which significantly increased screen time as many activities moved online, exacerbated concerns about the impact of tech use on teenagers' mental health. "Concerns about screen time and social media were high as we entered this crisis," the Common Sense Media report notes. "Now, in an unprecedented turn of events, virtually all adolescents have been directed online to meet their educational and social needs. Now more than ever, there is a need to flip the script around screen time from concerns over time spent online to how to safely connect adolescents to their schools, peers, family networks, and communities while also curating quality content and ensuring guardrails are in place."[222]

## Technology and Young Adults

Among young adults such as college students, a correlation between smartphone use and depression stands out. A Gallup poll showed that 52 percent of smartphone owners check their phones a few times an hour or more, and that young adults are the most frequent smartphone checkers.[223]

College students who described themselves as addicted to their smartphones were much more likely to suffer from depression than those who simply used smartphones without feeling addicted to mobile devices, according to a University of Illinois at Urbana-Champaign study featured in a Science Daily.com article.[224] The study's author, psychology professor Alejandro Lleras, notes, "People who self-described as having really addictive style behaviors toward the Internet and cellphones scored much higher on depression and anxiety scales."[225]

The article adds, "However, the researchers found no relationship between cellphone or Internet use and negative mental health outcomes among participants who used these technologies to escape from boredom. Thus, the motivation for going online is an important factor in relating technology usage to depression and anxiety. ... While the role of phones as comfort items is somewhat tenuous, the relationship between motivation for cellphone or Internet use and mental health warrants further exploration, Lleras said. Breaking addictive technology habits may provide an important supplemental treatment for addressing mental health issues such as general anxiety disorder or depression, he said."[226]

The distinction between healthy use of smartphones and addiction to smartphones is important. "We shouldn't be scared of people connecting online or talking on their phones," says Lleras. "The interaction with the device is not going to make you depressed if you are just using it when you are bored. This should go toward soothing some of that public anxiety over new technology."[227]

## Technology and Adults

Adults who overuse technology also may experience mental-health issues. The type of technology adults seem the most prone to overuse is the smartphone. Some people become so tied to their mobile devices that they carry their smartphones with them throughout each day, and even sleep with their phones close by at night. The Gallup poll results point out "the frequency with which Americans check their smartphones essentially means that they must be keeping their smartphones by their sides during the day. The data bear that assumption out: 81 percent of smartphone users say they keep their phone near them 'almost all the time during waking hours.' Americans' attachment to their smartphones is so strong that 63 percent report keeping it near them at night even while sleeping."[228]

According to statistics compiled by the digital wellness company Bagby, "A large majority of Americans (92 percent) believe that smartphone addiction is real. Although 60 percent of Americans think they touch their phone 100 times or less per day, the reality is that a typical user taps, touches, or swipes their phone a staggering 2,617 times per day."[229]

All that smartphone use can make us feel like we're connecting with others, yet actually harm the quality of our connections—and that can contribute to depression. "As technology continues to tighten its grip on our lives, the price for staying connected means that we lose the 'human' connection—our voices, touch, and facial expressions. So, when we reach for our smartphones, and think we are staying connected, we are actually drifting apart. The end result of this electronic urge leads to a preoccupation with, and need to reinforce this electronic high. ... The heaviest smartphone users exhibited the greatest degree of depression, anxiety and loneliness, and isolation."[230]

Lack of sleep can exacerbate depression, and smartphones often interfere with adults' sleep. "Mobile technology is perceived to cause negative effects to sleep. Of the respondents, 44 percent had been woken up by the noise, and 41 percent by the light from a mobile phone in the bedroom."[231]

Finally, a majority of American adults agree that technology overuse/addiction is affecting their mental health, and that it's important to do something about it. "[Two-thirds] of Americans say that they 'somewhat or strongly agree that periodically unplugging or taking a digital detox is important for their mental health."[232]

Dr. Robert Shulman, acting chair of the Department of Psychiatry and Behavioral Sciences at Rush University Medical Center in Chicago, Illinois sums up what technology does to human relationships. "Essentially, what we've done is taken a three-dimensional human relationship and turned it into a two-dimensional technical relationship, which is not a healthy thing to do," he says. "While some technology, such as health apps, can assist people with monitoring their well-being in a practical manner, overall, technology isn't designed to decrease isolation."[233]

# CHAPTER NINE
## DEPRESSION AND ADDICTION

**"Mental pain is less dramatic than physical pain, but it is more common and also more hard to bear. The frequent attempt to conceal mental pain increases the burden: it is easier to say 'My tooth is aching' than to say 'My heart is broken.'"**
—C.S. Lewis, British author, *The Problem of Pain*

Astrong connection exists between depression and substance abuse. Some people who are suffering from depression turn to alcohol and other drugs to cope, while some people who are struggling with an addiction to substances have underlying mental-health conditions such as depression. This relationship often results in a dual diagnosis of clinical depression along with alcohol/drug addiction.

"When it comes first, addiction can trigger the onset of depression," says Virginia Dale Manning, LPC-S, LCDC with GinMan Consulting in Houston, Texas. "People who are depressed feel hopeless and worthless and often can't break the cycle of addiction."[234]

"Mental illness and addiction often overlap. ... In fact, nearly 9 million people have a co-occurring disorder according to the Substance Abuse and Mental Health Services Administration. Yet, only 7 percent of these individuals get treatment for both conditions. And nearly 60 percent receive no treatment at all."[235]

Specifically, alcohol usage and depression are often linked together.

"What's more, one can make the other worse in a cycle that's pervasive and problematic if not addressed and treated. Alcohol use can cause or worsen symptoms of mood disorders. Depression may even cause people to begin consuming large amounts of alcohol. ... [P]eople with depression may attempt to self-medicate with alcohol."[236]

Dr. Nancy Irwin, a Los Angeles, California-based clinical psychologist and trauma and addictions specialist, notes that "[t]here is a cause-effect link. Alcohol is a depressant, so even if a person has no mood disorder, excessive alcohol can cause one. As well, many addicts began using/drinking to escape an undiagnosed depression. The intent was positive, and indeed they may have felt relief in the short term, but caused more depression by their attempt to self-medicate."[237]

A research study published in the *Journal of Substance Abuse Treatment* examines the correlation of depression with alcohol and drug use. The study shows "depression is associated with concurrent alcohol use and impairment and drug use and impairment. ... Depression was also related to future alcohol use and impairment, an earlier age of onset of alcohol use disorders, and higher treatment participation. ... Our findings indicate that depression is relevant both cross-sectionally and prospectively to measures of alcohol use and impairment."[238]

Unfortunately, substance abuse has always been common among those suffering from depression. "Because alcohol is a central nervous system depressant, the use of this drug tends to trigger depression symptoms like lethargy, sadness and hopelessness."[239] However, many of those battling depression often use alcohol or drugs to numb their pain or make them feel better. "Depression is all too often a gateway into drug and alcohol use. It's easy to see why. Those who experience feelings of depressions take alcohol and drugs in order to escape their negative emotions. But those who are clinically depressed are going to stay depressed if they do not seek treatment. And if these individuals are using drugs and alcohol on a regular basis, chances are their usage will soon turn into full-blown addiction as they continue in a vain attempt to self-medicate."[240]

"Both conditions [depression and addiction] disrupt the dopamine (uplifting neurotransmitter) balance in the brain," Dr. Irwin explains.

"After a certain length of time, the brain stops making dopamine because it has become reliant on the artificial (drugs, alcohol) 'lift.' This is why one needs more and more of the substance to achieve the desired effect. When one 'sleeps it off' and wakes up the next day, their baseline is depression. And they feel they must get back on the cycle of abuse to relieve the depression."

## Comorbidity

Patients who have a dual diagnosis of both depression and addiction are considered medically to have a comorbidity. "Comorbidity refers to the fact that two conditions, such as a specific mental health disorder and a substance use disorder, often co-exist together."[241]

One condition will often inflame the symptoms of the other condition. "To better understand how comorbidity is possible, it helps to recognize that both are chronic brain disorders.[242] This means a person's brain forms new neuropathways because of the substance abuse. "Just like diabetes or heart disease, a person with an addiction must manage his condition for the rest of his life. It is not as simple as stopping the drug use or alcohol condition. Many times, this is simply not possible. Likewise, the changes that take place in the brain due to substance abuse occur in the same brain areas that are impacted by depression, anxiety, schizophrenia, and bipolar disorder. Consequently, it should not be surprising that there is a high rate of comorbidity between addiction and other mental illnesses."[243]

A Psycom.net article points out the bi-directional relationship between depression and substance use addiction: "It's no secret that there is a strong connection between substance use and mental illness. The National Bureau of Economic Research reports that people who have been diagnosed with a mental illness at some point in life consume 69 percent of the nation's alcohol and 84 percent of the nation's cocaine."[244]

Depression and substance-use addiction can coexist in complex ways. "Alcohol may be a form of self-medication for people with depression. The 'burst' of energy from alcohol can be a welcome relief against some symptoms. For example, alcohol may temporarily reduce anxiety and lower inhibitions. However, the flip side is that people who frequently use alcohol are more likely to also be depressed. Drinking a lot may worsen these feelings, which may actually drive further drinking. Individuals with mental health conditions may be more likely to use alcohol as a treatment."[245]

According to some studies, military veterans may be more likely to struggle with post-traumatic stress disorder and depression and abuse alcohol. Some research has found that women who are depressed are more likely to binge drink. Experts note that previous trauma is another risk factor when predicting who will misuse alcohol while suffering from depression. "This is true for adults as well as children and young adults. Children who have major depression as a child may drink earlier in life, according to one study."[246]

Here are some factors, according to Psycom.net, that may contribute to depression or alcohol abuse:

- **Genetics.** A family history of either alcoholism or depression may increase a person's risk.
- **Personality.** Those who have a more negative outlook on life, suffer from low self-esteem or have trouble with social situations also appear more likely to develop depression or misuse alcohol.
- **Personal history.** People with abuse, relationship troubles or trauma in their backgrounds may have a predilection to depression or alcohol abuse.[247]

Depression and substance-use addiction can co-occur for a variety of reasons. For example, drug abuse can trigger mental-illness symptoms while mental disorders can push a person into alcohol or drug abuse as a way to self-medicate. "There also is some evidence that indicates that addictions and mental illnesses are caused by underlying brain deficits, genetic influences, and/or exposure to trauma early in life. For instance, it is estimated that 40 to 60 percent of a person's vulnerability to addiction can be attributed to genetics. There also are several regions of the human genome that have been linked to an increased risk both for substance abuse and mental illness. ... People who are physically or emotionally traumatized are at a much higher risk of substance use disorders."[248]

Research from the study published in the *Journal of Substance*

*Abuse Treatment* reveals "[h]igh rates of depression are common among individuals with alcohol use disorders (AUD), particularly alcohol dependence. Data from the National Comorbidity Survey estimated the lifetime prevalence of major depression to be nearly one quarter (24.3 %) among alcohol dependent men and nearly one half (48.5%) among alcohol dependent women, exceeding the prevalence rates among individuals without AUD."[249]

## The Pandemic's Push

The coronavirus pandemic has exacerbated the dangerous relationship between depression and substance abuse, according to a research study from the New York University School of Global Public Health (NYU GPH) in New York City. "This increase in drinking, particularly among people with anxiety and depression, is consistent with concerns that the pandemic may be triggering an epidemic of problematic alcohol use," says Ariadna Capasso, a doctoral student at NYU GPH and the study's lead author.[250]

"COVID-19 has created many stressors, including isolation and the disruption of routines, economic hardship, illness, and fear of contagion, and studies suggest that people are drinking more during the pandemic."[251]

Those who have existing mental-health conditions can be particularly susceptible to alcohol misuse in times of stress. NYU GPH researchers asked participants in an online survey in March and April 2020 about this correlation. "Of the 5,850 survey respondents who said that they drink, 29 percent reported increasing their alcohol use during the pandemic, while 19.8 percent reported drinking less and 51.2 percent reported no change. People with depression were 64 percent more likely to increase their alcohol intake, while those with anxiety were 41 percent more likely to do so."[252]

## Treating Both

There is hope that people with both depression and substance-abuse addictions can find healing and greater well-being. Although the connections between the two conditions are complex, people can successfully treat both—especially if they are treated simultaneously. "The good news is that treating both alcohol misuse and depression can make both conditions better. ... As one improves, symptoms of the other may improve, too. It isn't, however, a quick and easy process. It's often a lifelong commitment, but one that can improve your life, health, and well-being in the long term."[253]

Virginia Manning recommends patients start by getting a comprehensive assessment from a qualified health professional. "This will help determine the level of treatment by answering questions like when did it start, how severe is the depression, how much is the person using or drinking per day, etc.," she says. "It will give you a very clear picture of where to start."

Dr. Irwin also points out how important it is to detox under the guidance of a medical professional, especially for those also suffering from depression. "Self-detoxing or cold turkey can lead to seizures and even death. After an appropriate detox, there are a multitude of helpful treatments to maintain sobriety, such as trauma resolution, behavioral therapy, psychotherapy (CBT in particular is extremely effective), and in some cases, medication," she explains.

Research supports co-treatments for the best possible outcome. "[E]arly detection and treatment of both conditions can greatly improve the person's recovery and quality of life. However, it is important to note that people who have both an addiction and another mental illness often have symptoms that are more persistent, severe and resistant to treatment compared with patients who have either disorder alone. For this reason, maintaining sobriety may be very difficult for them."[254]

Treatment plans for depressed and addicted patients try to solve complex problems. "What makes a dual diagnosis so hard to treat is that each disorder can intensify the symptoms of the other. Drinking excessive amounts of alcohol, for instance, is not going to make the depression better; in fact, it will make the condition more serious. And conversely, if a person is an alcoholic, their depression will likely keep them from attaining the proper mindset to overcome their addiction to alcohol. There is a high level of complexity involved in treating the dual diagnosis patient."[255]

One example of someone who has successfully sought treatment for both depression and substance-abuse addiction is the singer Joanna Levesque (known professionally as JoJo). She grew up watching her father struggle with an addiction to opioid drugs. At eighteen, JoJo began drinking alcohol to the point of blackouts. Then, shortly afterward, she was diagnosed with major depressive disorder. Now, after about a decade of treatment for her depression, which included counseling therapy, antidepressant medication, exercise, yoga, and journaling, both her mental health and her drinking habits have improved.

"Because there is a history of mental health issues in my family, I didn't feel any shame seeking help," JoJo says in *People* magazine. "Those of us who have a predisposition toward depression or a chemical imbalance— sometimes we just need a little help. ... I developed a different relationship with my body that was on my terms, and I looked at what I could control as opposed to what was out of my control."[256]

Jojo recalled her father telling her "just you wait" until addiction took over her life, but "I remember telling him, 'I don't accept that as my fate. I don't accept that just because this in my DNA that this has to be my future.' I'll never forget that. ... [Now] I am actively practicing self-love. It's not just something you arrive at—I need to really work at it."[257]

Often, family members can be key to helping someone overcome depression and addiction. "Family members/friends of loved ones who struggle with addictions can attend Al-Anon or Nar-Anon meetings to learn how to be supportive in a healthy way, set boundaries, stop enabling or trying to control, and more," says Dr. Irwin. "The co-addict position (or the loved one of a depressive person) is a tough role to be in, and therapy can help, as well as support groups, along with a balanced, healthy lifestyle."

The most common treatments for both conditions include: antidepressant medications, medications to lower alcohol cravings, time in a rehabilitation facility, cognitive behavior therapy (CBT), and support groups. "Treating one of these conditions may improve symptoms for both. However, for the best results, your doctor will likely treat them together. ... Treating both will help ease symptoms of both. However, not treating both can make the conditions worse."[258]

For patients with a dual diagnosis of depression and substance-abuse addiction, a comprehensive treatment plan is needed. Medication like antidepressants frequently are more effective alongside behavior support and counseling. Many times, intensive outpatient or inpatient treatment is necessary to control addiction and replace those cravings with healthier coping strategies for depression. "While relapse may and often occurs, people generate the greatest odds for long-term recovery when they treat both the depression and the substance use."[259]

During the pandemic, which exacerbated both depression and substance use addiction for some people, increasing treatment options became important. For example, NYU GBH researchers encouraged telehealth and other means to overcome barriers to mental-health and substance-use services. "Lessons we've learned from previous disasters show us that intervening early for unhealthy substance use is critical and could help lessen the pandemic's impact on mental health," says Ralph DiClemente, chair of the Department of Social and Behavioral Sciences at NYU GBH and the study's senior author.[260]

New and innovative treatments for both depression and addiction may be on the horizon. One possibility could involve brain-computer interface. "Tesla and SpaceX CEO Elon Musk claims that his new Neuralink brain-computer interface could cure depression and addiction."[261] Musk says his Neuralink company "had developed a 'sewing machine-link' device that could connect brains directly to computers."[262]

Will Neuralink be able to retrain the brain's response to addiction or depression? Musk seems to think so. "Early versions of the Neuralink system have reportedly been tested on animals and human trials are expected to take place this year. Musk reportedly hopes that the device will help humans achieve symbiosis with artificial intelligence."[263]

No matter what treatment plan patients pursue, it's vital that they seek help for both their depression and addiction—and keep trying to heal however they can. "Finding the right approach to pharmacological treatment can take time and patience, but with the help of qualified staff who are trained in dual diagnosis treatment, prescription drugs can provide valuable support. Support, encouragement and motivation are essential tools in the battle against depression and substance abuse."[264]

When Manning's mother self-medicated with alcohol along with her psychotropic medications to mask her depression, Manning says she wished she had sought help to better understand what her mother was going through. "You have to build your own knowledge and your strength when dealing with someone battling depression and addiction," she says. "Their addiction and depression affects not just them but family, work, and all their relationships. It's important for everyone to know the warning signs and how depression fits into addiction in order to help those we love."

# CHAPTER TEN
## DOCTORS AND DEPRESSION

**"The best thing you can do to make your depression treatment a success is to find a doctor who will work with you and whom you can trust."**
—Dr. Wes Burgess, English author, in *The Depression Answer Book*

People suffering from depression can seek treatment for the disease from a variety of health-care professionals, including psychiatrists, psychologists, and social workers. Choosing the right type of provider is crucial for building a strong doctor/patient relationship that promotes healing.

Most people start the journey with their internist or primary-care physician. If you have classic depression symptoms, such as those listed on page 20 in Chapter 1, then your internist or primary-care doctor will likely refer you to a psychiatrist or psychologist. What I've found is that you as the patient often have to educate the educators because sometimes internists aren't up to speed on depression treatment. The internists or a psychiatrist could treat the depression and may be successful. However, someone like a psychopharmacologist—a psychiatrist who specializes in medication management—may provide a more focused regimen that will target your depression more thoroughly. Sometimes treatment by a psychopharmacologist is combined with that of a talk therapist (see Chapter 17 for more on talk therapy and depression). A psychopharmacologist will go through a lot of material, such as a patient's full medical and family history, that might be relevant to the illness, especially if there are family members who have received depression diagnosis and been treated effectively with certain medications.

The ultimate goal of the search for the right treatment is for patients to find health-care professionals who will partner with them throughout the healing process. "The two of you need to work as a team, making decisions, sharing information, and discussing the benefits and risks of different treatment options. It should be a two-way street with mutual participation in all decisions."[265]

### The Role of Primary-Care Doctors

Patients will probably begin their search for the right health-care providers by speaking with their primary-care doctor. After hearing the basic details about a patient's individual concerns about depression, a primary-care doctor can make recommendations and referrals to help develop an effective treatment plan.

Many primary-care physicians prescribe medications, such as antidepressants or sedatives, to patients with depression, but their experience with depression medications or depression treatment might be more limited. For example, primary-care doctors often have knowledge of one or two antidepressants, and can be "less rigorous in their diagnosis of depression than psychiatrists are."[266]

Health-care experts like the Mayo Clinic recommend asking for a doctor referral from a primary-care doctor. Additional potential sources of therapist referrals or recommendations include health insurance companies, friends, family members, clergy, and professional mental-health associations.[267]

### The Role of Psychopharmacology

One key question for depressed people to consider when searching for the right health-care professional is whether or not they are willing to try medication to treat their disease. Many medical professionals who treat depression also are psychopharmacologists who use medications and psychology to treat mental disorders.

Depressed patients should educate themselves about the psychopharmacology of any drugs they're considering taking. It can be helpful to ask doctors basic psychopharmacology questions such as:

- How will the medication work in my body?
- How long will the medication stay in my body?
- Will the medication interact with other medications, and if so, how?

Any medical doctor who can prescribe drugs to treat mental conditions (like depression) must be thoroughly educated in psychopharmacology. "In a generic sense, any physician who treats patients with psychotropic medication is a psychopharmacologist. … Physicians who have completed residency training after medical school have a high level of understanding and expertise in pharmacology, including psychopharmacology. Psychiatrists (who have completed four years of advanced training after medical school) have an even higher level of understanding and expertise in psychopharmacology."[268]

Once patients decide to pursue medications to treat their depression, they also should consider what the goal is of using those medications. Patients should consider combining medications with therapy as psychopharmacology has been found to be more effective when combined with psychotherapy. "Yes, taking medication at some point may be a crucial part of the patient's responsibility for getting better, but it is no substitute for real psychotherapy. How psychopharmacology and its implicit psychology is understood and employed in psychotherapy is key: Is medication used merely to deaden metaphorical demons? Or to support confronting and coming to terms with them?"[269]

## The Role of Psychiatrists

Psychiatrists are the most experienced of the health-care professionals who treat depression. Basically, a psychiatrist diagnoses, counsels, treats, and prescribes medication for those with mental-health disorders.

Many times psychiatrists are the best option for depression treatment.

"Compared with other professionals, they usually have the most experience treating patients with severe depression. In addition to their understanding of the wealth of medications used to treat unipolar major depression, psychiatrists are the only medical doctors who are fully trained in psychotherapy for depression. ... They should be able to discuss all the relevant benefits, side effects, and risks of whatever treatment you choose. They may offer to do both medications and psychotherapy together in the same session."[270]

The drawback is that it typically is costs more to see psychiatrists. The Mayo Clinic advises patients to check the details of their health-insurance policies or other health coverage (like Medicare or Medicaid) when researching potential treatment options so they can make informed decisions. But for those who can afford it, getting depression treatment from psychiatrists may be best for patients with severe depression. "In general, the more severe your symptoms or complex your diagnosis, the more expertise and training you need to look for in a mental health provider."[271]

### The Role of Psychologists

Psychologists are not medical doctors like psychiatrists, so they can't prescribe antidepressant drugs unless they have a special license. However, they do receive extensive training in how to treat depression. A psychologist diagnoses and treats many mental-health disorders, and provides psychological counseling in group settings or individually.

The training for psychologists involves earning a doctoral degree (a PhD) and completing a year of practical internship. "They may be the only sources for behavioral or cognitive psychotherapy in your community. Professional psychologists do not receive extensive training in the biology or pharmacology of depression in the brain and nervous system. Professional psychologists' fees are usually less than psychiatrists' fees and more than counselors' fees."[272]

Psychologists can be experts at treating depression through counseling therapy, but usually refer their patients who need antidepressant medication to other health-care providers like physicians, physician assistants, and nurses who can prescribe and monitor drug therapy in conjunction with the counseling they provide. This means many patients with depression may need more than one doctor to assist in managing their illness—one for counseling and one for prescribing medications.

Most state laws restrict prescription writing to medical doctors only. "A few states have given doctoral psychologists the ability to prescribe a few drugs, but they do not receive the extensive training in human biology and psychopharmacology that is provided to medical doctors."[273]

### The Role of Social Workers

Social workers who are trained to help evaluate and treat depression also can help patients through counseling. In addition, social workers often deal with the broad scope of lifestyle changes that promote healing in depressed patients' lives. So if depressed people want help with general life issues—such as advice on how to improve family relationships or help managing time and energy in healthier ways—social workers might be able to provide that assistance. And social workers can be valuable resources for patients who want help accessing services from large organizations like hospitals or government agencies.

The social workers who treat mental-health conditions such as depression "provide assessment, psychological counseling, and a range of other services, depending on their licensing and training; are not licensed to prescribe medication [and] may work with another provider who can prescribe medication if needed."[274]

Social workers can help patients navigate federal, state, and local services available to those with depression and their families. Often, social workers have training in family psychotherapy. "Licensed clinical social workers (LCSWs) have extra training in psychotherapy and mental illness. Some social workers provide service at low or deferred cost."[275]

Wherever you begin your journey, finding the right doctor to guide you on your way to recovery might take some time. My advice is to go to the top of the food chain when it comes to finding help for depression, and psychopharmacologists are at the top. Unfortunately, many people suffering from depression haven't had access to a psychopharmacologist, either because they didn't realize such doctors existed or because they didn't have one practicing in their area.

We can't lose sight of the fact that the most important thing is for those suffering from depression to seek medical assistance, whether from a primary-care doctor, a psychologist, a psychiatrist, or a psychopharmacologist.

# CHAPTER ELEVEN
## PATIENTS, DOCTORS, AND DEPRESSION

**"Just like other illnesses, depression can be treated so that people can live happy, active lives."**
—Tom Bosley, American actor

Just making a doctor's appointment can be difficult for those suffering from depression, but thankfully, in my case, I knew something was wrong and that something warranted a trip to see a doctor. But I also was lucky in that my first doctor was a psychopharmacologist working as an internist for psychopharmacologist Dr. William Scheftner. His experience allowed him to diagnose what I had and to help me. Under his care—and on several medications—I was out of my first depression within six months. Because the internist was leaving the area, he referred me to Dr. Scheftner for follow-up care. At that point, I didn't realize that I would have more episodes of depression; I was just grateful to have gotten through the depression rather quickly and "back to normal."

I realize that not everyone suffering from depression has the luxury of sticking with the same doctor throughout their entire life, but that happened to me with Dr. Scheftner. I started going to him when I was 24 years old. He has seen me through my whole adult lifetime and the various depressions I've had over the years.

Through my experiences with depression, I learned that patients should know as much as they can about the disease and the medical professionals providing treatment. The biggest thing for me—and the reason that I was able to persevere and understand things—is that right at the beginning, my doctor explained to me what I had. In our brains, we have chemicals that make us feel good, such as endorphins (a runner's high, for example), and others that create how we feel overall. When you are depressed, the synapses between brain cells are closed, preventing the proper flow of natural brain chemicals that make us feel good. The moment I heard Dr. Scheftner's explanation, the disease ceased to be a mystery and became something with a name, something that could be addressed and treated.

Here are some other factors I recommend keeping in mind when choosing a doctor to treat your depression:

- **Type of doctor.** Although primary-care physicians and psychologists know how to treat genetic depression, they don't have the experience of a psychopharmacologist. It's best to find the most specialized doctor you can to treat your depression in order to achieve a faster recovery. (See Chapter 10 for more on what each doctor can and can't do for depressed patients.)
- **Role.** It's the doctor's role to help a patient recover, and it's the patient's role to do what the doctor recommends, especially in terms of taking medications, etc. "I always tell my patients that if you're alive, I can get you better," says Dr. Scheftner. "But if you're dead, I can't do anything."
- **Explanations.** Doctors should clarify their diagnosis and instructions, not just in clinical terms, but in a way that the patient can understand. It's invaluable to have a doctor who takes the time to explain what's happening to the brain of a depressed person, what causes the depression, and what steps are being taken to treat the disease.
- **Listening.** Doctors should listen attentively to patients. Finding a doctor who will take the time to really hear what you are saying can be a crucial part of your recovery.
- **Assertiveness.** You want a doctor who will prescribe an ag-

gressive treatment when necessary to achieve the best possible outcome, according to Dr. Scheftner. Treatment plans should be tailored to the patient, and patients who don't respond to initial therapies should receive additional interventions.

When you decide to seek medical help for your depression, ask your primary-care physician for a referral or call a local teaching hospital for a list of doctors in the psychiatry department who treat depression. If this seems too insurmountable a task because of your illness, ask a family member or friend for assistance.

If you are suffering from depression, having the right relationship with your medical professional is essential to your recovery. I strongly urge you to find a doctor who will be more than someone who diagnoses you, but also someone who is beside you and committed to helping you get through your journey out of depression.

# CHAPTER TWELVE
## FAMILIES, DOCTORS, AND DEPRESSION

**"My hope is that one day, doctors would be able to run a test and know which medication would help the depressed patient. That way the patient would get better faster."**
—My mother, Dona Litzsinger

Families with a member who has depression can feel pulled in many different directions. They can be as overwhelmed by the disease as the person suffering from it. What's essential is that they understand as much as possible what doctors can do to help their depressed family member—such knowledge will help the family to provide as much encouragement and support as possible.

I was very fortunate in that my family was absolutely supportive and there for me, but learning that supportive role took many years. They knew me and they knew the symptoms of depression. My father and brother eventually met with my psychopharmacologist privately to let him know that it didn't seem like the medications were working because they could see something that I couldn't during my depression. "All of Mark's siblings helped him whenever they could," said my mother. "We're a very close family and when anyone's in trouble, we all pitch in to help. In that way, Mark was very lucky to have that support."

But my family had different views about the doctor's role—and theirs. "The doctor was helpful as best he could," says my sister Robin. "However,

I'm not sure he told us anything that was different from what we already knew about how we could help Mark." My brother, Todd, felt challenged in his supportive role, noting that "Mark literally didn't want us involved with his therapies—medical or general. But I kept encouraging him to let us get involved, especially in the early days before the depression developed into a major episode."

Sometimes, people with depression become very defensive. I know that's how I responded when my family tried to help me. My family created a roadmap of options to help me through the depression. My father and Todd discussed different things that might help me overcome the depression with my doctor, including signs that could indicate I was sliding back into a depressive episode. In my final, worst depression at 47 years old, my father and brother met with my doctor on their own because they were concerned that I wasn't improving.

"We sat down with the doctor and said, 'What can we do? It's gotten to the point that he can't take care of himself,'" remembers Todd. "We really felt that he was a danger to others because he wasn't of sound mind. And he was also jeopardizing his job because he couldn't function and do his job well."

That's the kind of advocacy patients need on their side because the doctors may not be fully aware of how bad someone's depression has become. "I think sometimes when you've seen someone for so long ... there is a little bit of tunnel vision, and they don't see things as we see them every day," notes Todd. "Mark probably put on a good show for the doctor. So our intervention was very important to get the doctor to realize that Mark's depression was jeopardizing Mark's long-term health."

It's also crucial to let your loved one's doctor or medical team know if the person is suicidal. More than 90 percent of those who commit suicide have been diagnosed with clinical depression or another mental disorder.[276] Risk factors include previous suicide attempts, a family history of suicide or mental disorder/substance abuse, family violence, physical or sexual abuse, and accessible firearms (see "Suicide Warning Signs" for more signs). "We're thankful that we never had a feeling of Mark feeling low in a way that he would want to off himself. I've seen that with other people, but I never felt or saw that with him," says Todd. "And for that we are grateful."

Family members can be a valuable advocate with the doctor when depression prevents the patient from doing so. "I remember hearing this from Mark, 'Well, my doctor is adjusting this. My doctor is adjusting that,'" recalls Todd. "During this third episode, we went to talk to the doctor because we realized that the medication adjustments just weren't working. That's when he [the doctor] suggested electroconvulsive therapy." (See Chapter 16 for more about shock therapy.)

If my family hadn't seen that the medications weren't working and knew that something else needed to be tried, I might not have gotten help as soon as I did. I was very glad I had given permission for my family to talk with my doctors because of the extra support they provided during my depression episodes.

## Suicide Warning Signs[277]

If your loved one suffers from depression, there's a chance he or she might become suicidal. Any talk of suicide should be taken seriously. You can get help by calling 800-SUICIDE (800-784-2433), 800-273-TALK (800-273-8255), or 800-799-4889 (for the hearing impaired).

Here are the warning signs of suicide. Contact a medical professional or call the suicide hotline immediately if you suspect your loved one might be contemplating suicide.

- Constant talk or thoughts of death, including talk of suicide
- Clinical depression (deep sadness, trouble sleeping/eating, loss of interest) that worsens
- Tempting "death" by risky behavior (running red lights, driving too fast)
- Loss of interest in what used to interest the person, such as a change in hobby or activity participation

- Comments about worthlessness, helplessness, or hopelessness
- Putting affairs in order (updating wills, organizing papers, etc.)
- Saying phrases like "I want out" or "It would be better if I wasn't around"
- Drastic, sudden change from very sad to very happy or calm
- Telling people "goodbye"
- Past suicide attempts

# CHAPTER THRITEEN
## DEPRESSION TREATMENTS
## IN THE TWENTIETH CENTURY

**"The beauty of depression, if there is one, is that the depressed person rarely remembers anything of the episode when they come out of it."**
—My father, Dick Litzsinger

Treatments for depression changed a great deal during the twentieth century, progressing from the advent of psychotherapy through the invention of antidepressant medications. The last century saw myriad different approaches to treating the disease, many of which proved beneficial to patients.

At the beginning of the twentieth century, the relatively new field of psychoanalysis, which emerged in the late nineteenth century, started exploring how to treat depressed people without medication. Spearheaded by pioneering psychiatrists Sigmund Freud and Carl Jung, this process involved treating patients by listening and talking.

Around the 1950s, the invention of antidepressant medications gradually grew to become the most popular form of physical treatment for depression, replacing earlier physical treatments such as shock therapy and surgery.

It wasn't until 1980 that the disease of depression was officially classified as a separate condition that could be treated distinctly from other mental-health conditions. "There was no specific disease of depression prior to the 1980 edition of the American Psychiatric Association's *Diagnostic and Statistical Manual-III (DSM-III)*—although there were disease categories of manic-depressive psychosis and individual melancholia that shared a few of the same features as the current diagnosis of depression."[278]

By the end of the twentieth century, both psychoanalysis and antidepressant medications had gained ground as popular treatments for depressed patients. The two treatments often went hand-in-hand as part of a comprehensive plan to treat depression by improving every aspect of a person's overall health—body, mind, and spirit.

"In general medicine, the average primary-care physician used to take the attitude of avoidance when confronted with a patient with depression symptoms," says Dr. Pollack, chief medical officer and vice president of clinical affairs for Neuroscience of Myriad Genetics in Mason, Ohio. "It was too difficult to help such a person. But now that has changed with the realization about opportunities to screen patients for depression and the recognition of ways to help those more easily."

A closer look at the treatments of the last century will lay the groundwork for the way depression is being treated today. Much of the work of the twentieth century guided depression treatments away from the inhumane and sometimes barbaric practices of the past toward more enlightened treatment. "Currently, we now enjoy a more nuanced view of the person that encompasses development and lifestyle issues as well as the context of how people interact with their environment," explains Dr. Pollack.

Here is a timeline of depression treatments.

### 1910s/1920s: A Focus on Alleviating Symptoms

During the earliest decades of the twentieth century, most people with a mental-illness diagnosis of any kind, including depression, found themselves in mental hospitals. With depression not yet classified as a distinct disease, doctors and therapists simply focused on depressed people's symptoms (such as sorrow and lethargy) with whatever treatments they thought could best alleviate those symptoms. For some, this meant physical treatment plans, such as changing their diet, getting more sleep, and following bathing or exercise regimens. For others, that meant counseling through the new field of psychoanalysis.

Most practitioners focused their study on the alleviation of symptoms at this time, in large part because disease concepts had yet to be well defined. "But though both psychiatrists and neurologists emphasized the relief of symptoms, symptom relief meant different things in different treatment settings."[279]

Generally speaking, psychiatrists favored allopathic treatment ("a system of medical practice that aims to combat disease by use of remedies [such as drugs or surgery] producing effects different from or incompatible with those produced by the disease being treated").[280] This practice led to creative and sometimes therapies, including gastric lavage—the washing out of the stomach with sterile water or a saline solution—for indigestion and constipation. Extreme methods were used to activate lethargic patients or calm agitated patients. The goal of treatment was to get the patient well enough to leave the hospital. "Although psychiatrists focused on the hospital context, neurologists in the first part of the century treated depressive symptoms in the same way as other types of symptoms, particularly with an emphasis on rest and feeding."[281]

The most common type of treatment for depressed patients during these years was psychoanalysis. In this type of therapy, the patient reclined on a couch nearly every day for an hour with the analyst out of view but in the room. While relaxing, "the patient simply allowed her mind to wander and spoke whatever thoughts came into her head, however odd, embarrassing, vexing, or socially unacceptable."[282]

The analyst would then analyze the stream of talk for patterns and inconsistencies before making suggestions to the patient as to their meaning or implications. "Through this iterative [repetitive] process of free thought, speaking aloud the thoughts, and interacting with the analyst, the patient would gradually gain access to the repressed thoughts lying in her unconscious, bring them to the realm of the conscious, and resolve the decades-old fears and anxieties with a sensible adult framework."[283]

Psychoanalysis fell out of favor for depression treatments in the latter part of the twentieth century, but doctors are now realizing the important link between mind and body, and seek to restore a person's whole being through various treatments. But a century ago, the tenuous results of psychoanalysis on depression patients paved the way for more radical methods.

### 1930s/1940s: Drastic Measures

A growing sense of dissatisfaction about the effectiveness of depression treatments coupled with alarm about the despair many depressed patients suffered in mental institutions led to the development of more drastic depression treatments. By the 1930s and 1940s, Americans revolted over the state of big psychiatric hospitals because of overcrowding, often horrific living conditions, and patients' overall hopeless attitudes.

These institutions promoted an assortment of extreme interventions, including psychosurgery and convulsive therapies. The new treatments often involved highly invasive procedures, such as lobotomies (surgically destroying the frontal lobes of patients' brains), electroconvulsive therapy (applying electric shocks to patients' brains), and comas induced through insulin drugs. Patients who weren't experiencing significant healing from depression through psychoanalysis frequently would be referred for these more severe treatments.

Although shock treatments and surgery did help alleviate depression in some people, both types of treatments were controversial. "Many patients, particularly those who had suffered severe, prolonged, and crippling depression, improved dramatically [after shock treatment]."[284] Meanwhile, lobotomy surgeries—a procedure both crude and destructive—were labeled unnecessarily harsh by detractors. However, that criticism didn't stop these treatments from continuing throughout the 1930s and '40s before declining in the '50s as doctors began prescribing antidepressant medications.

Psychoanalysis continued to be a popular form of treatment for less severely depressed patients during this era, yet because of a shortage of trained psychiatrists, many people who needed treatment for their depression didn't get it. "This psychotherapeutic reality is, indeed, grotesque. Millions of people need treatment, and only a few thousands can get it—at an exorbitant price and a tremendous sacrifice of time," wrote psychiatrist Martin Gumpert in 1946.[285]

## 1950s: Antidepressant Medications Arrive

Patients around the middle of the twentieth century typically sought either psychotherapy or medications to treat their depression—but not both. That was because physicians at that time thought that depression could be neatly categorized into two distinct types, each of which required a different type of treatment. "Influenced by hundreds of years of back and forth debate as to whether depression was best thought of as a mental or physical problem, and by increasing knowledge of the brain and brain chemistry, the medical community of the 1950s and '60s accepted a classification that divided depression into subtypes based on supposed causes of the disorder."[286]

Endogenous depression was thought to come from within the body and caused by a physical problem or genetics. Reactive or neurotic depression was thought to be triggered by a significant environmental change, such as job loss, death of a spouse, etc. People diagnosed with endogenous depression sought physical treatments (medications), while people diagnosed with neurotic depression sought mental/emotional treatments (psychotherapy).

Antidepressant medications arrived on the scene in the 1950s. "In 1952, doctors noticed that a tuberculosis [TB] medication (isoniazid) was also useful in treating people with depression. Shortly after this significant finding, the practice of using medications to treat mental illness gained full steam."[287] From that point on, medications became the first line of defense in mental-illness treatment.

"This development corresponded with a shift in medical thinking from depression as a purely emotional issue to a brain disease fixable by medication," notes Dr. Pollack. "The discovery of the antidepressant use of a TB medication helped that transition along."

The two early antidepressant drugs Imipramine and Marsilid established the foundations of how doctors understood and prescribed medications to treat depression during the late 1950s. Scientists used the action of these antidepressant drugs to draw conclusions about the nature of the illness. Imipramine and Marsilid worked differently, but led to the same result in the end.

Those drugs trigger larger amounts of the neurotransmitter norepinephrine to conjugate in the synapses (micro-spaces between the brain's nerve cells) which allow the brain cells to "talk" via chemical gestures. "Drugs in Impiramine's family, the tricyclics, do this by blocking the re-absorption, or reuptake, of norepinephrine from the synapse back into the nerve cells around it. Drugs in Marsilid's family, which came to be known as 'MAO inhibitors,' or MAOIs, do it by dampening the action of an enzyme that breaks down certain neurotransmitters, norepinephrine included. MAO inhibitors also boost brain levels of another neurotransmitter, serotonin. Later research confirmed that tricyclic antidepressants do so too."[288]

The field of psychotherapy grew significantly during this era, as many new types of counseling therapies emerged. Newly minted psychotherapists from a wide variety of backgrounds began to create therapy schools based on their own experimentation with different therapeutic techniques. Most of these approaches differed only slightly in techniques but a few provided innovative treatment. "One new technique emphasized cognitive processes over emotional processes, for example, and another required behavioral interventions instead of psychological interventions."[289]

"This [new technique] was partly due to the heavy influence of European psychoanalytic thinking, which thankfully didn't permeate the entire United States," says Dr. Scheftner.

## 1960s/1970s: New Drugs and Psychotherapy

Throughout the 1960s and '70s, pharmaceutical companies developed a plethora of new medications to treat depression, and psychiatrists began to counsel depressed patients according to a treatment approach called cognitive-behavioral therapy. New medications were based on the two families of antidepressants that had emerged in the 1950s (tricyclics and MAOIs). These medications included Nardil, Pamelor, and Elavil, as well as drugs in a new medication family called benzodiazapenes (popularly known as tranquilizers).

These tranquilizers (such as Valium and Librium) were at first presented as medications for anyone who was seeking stress relief, not as drugs targeted to any specific disease. Tranquilizers were "originally marketed to ease the strains of corporate life for hard-driving businessmen" and then "turned into a phenomenon"[290] as people with mental illness began using tranquilizers to treat their symptoms. "When lithium was released for general use in the United States, it was significant because of its effectiveness for people with bipolar disorder," says Dr. Scheftner.

The popularity of tranquilizers led more people to seek treatment for depression, even when they had a mild case. "The availability of an easy fix for a common mental problem brought many new cases out of the woodwork, and demand for psychiatric services increased."[291] Because tranquilizers could be prescribed by doctors after just one appointment, many depressed people opted to take them for short-term relief of their symptoms rather than participate in ongoing psychotherapy. As Katherine Sharpe asks in *Coming of Age on Zoloft*: "Why spend long years analyzing your problems when you can pop a pill and watch them melt away?"[292]

However, these drugs had numerous side effects and it often took many weeks to find the right dosage. That's what happened to me with my first round of antidepressants. I'd tell the doctor what was going on, that I was having ruminations and obsessive-compulsive behaviors, and he'd recommend tweaks to the medications. In a normal person, you would see some lifting of your illness within two to three weeks, but in my case it might be six to eight weeks before we'd know whether a medication was effective.

The procedures in place at this time meant weeks of waiting and adjusting dosages before the patient had any change to his illness. This treatment was based on a regimen that was proven over time. But depending on the patient, the doctors might tweak the dosage or try different combinations in the hope that a new drug might push the main drug to do what it was supposed to do. What worked for one person might not work for the other. It was a trial-and-error process.

Adding to the frustration was the fact that to switch drugs, the patient had to wait for the previous medicine to work its way out of his or her system before starting the new medication. I always likened it to drying out like an alcoholic for a week or two before starting the new medication. When I was in the drying-out period, I was probably not getting any better and I was more likely getting a little worse because I wasn't on anything.

"The shift in the '60s away from the psycho-dynamic towards increasing usage of medications to treat depression was significant," says Dr. Pollack. That change also led to more depressed people seeking alternative methods of treatment.

Not only did depressed people in the 1960s and '70s seek easier ways to treat their disease with medication, they also tried to find easier ways to treat depression through psychotherapy (counseling). "The basic concepts that underlie the cognitive theory of depression were developed during the 1960s."[293] That approach to treating depression, which is also sometimes referred to as cognitive-behavioral therapy, focuses on the connections between the patient's thoughts, feelings, and actions. The goal of cognitive therapy is for patients to learn to identify and change distorted thinking patterns, inaccurate beliefs, and unhelpful behaviors.

This new, practical approach to counseling emerged as "there was considerable dissatisfaction with psychoanalytic theory and treatment."[294] Why? Because of "its length, expense, and lack of superior efficacy over the briefer forms of therapy."[295]

That dissatisfaction with psychoanalysis set the stage for shorter and less-expensive counseling sessions to treat depression. "Thus, the controversy over the effectiveness of psychodynamic psychotherapy as well as the increased demand for brief and effective treatments created a receptive environment in the 1970s for alternative approaches to depression."[296] These new, briefer treatments often involved trying to solve specific problems in depressed patients' lives to reduce their stress levels, which counselors hoped would in turn reduce the intensity of their depression.

However, during these two decades, the tide turned toward a more biological reason for depression when the first set of relatively comprehensive diagnostic criteria in psychiatry was published in the medical journal Archives of General Psychiatry. "The point is you went from a diagnosis that was not well-specified to one that had specific criteria to be met," explains Dr. Scheftner.

## 1980s: The Age of Prozac

During the 1980s, patients suffering from severe depression still took antidepressants prescribed by psychiatrists or doctors, but those with mild depression began backing away from tranquilizers. The stage was set for a new type of medication to emerge.

Tranquilizers had declined in popularity as "stories about tranquilizer addiction had begun to appear regularly in the press, and the public's love of tranquilizers started to turn into fear and ridicule. For the time being, Americans with minor mental problems were left without a go-to medication."[297]

In 1987, the "blockbuster drug" Prozac burst on the scene, fueling the dramatically increased popularity of antidepressant medications in the late twentieth century. "By 1987, about 1.8 percent of Americans purchased an antidepressant each year. That's not nothing, but it's hardly the explosive proliferation that would begin in the 1990s [because of Prozac]."[298]

Prozac's introduction ushered in a new biological age. Prozac became "the most commercially successful drug in the history of the pharmaceutical industry."[299] This antidepressant regulated the brain's serotonin levels and had few side effects. Previously, psychiatrists typically wrote prescriptions for antidepressants in order to supervise the often tricky dosage. Now, Prozac promised an easy "one pill a day forever" routine that enticed general practitioners and internists to pick up their pen to write prescriptions for the drug, bypassing the traditional method of referring the patient to a trained psychiatrist or counselor. During the ten years after Prozac's debut, the number of patients seeking mental-health treatment from general practitioners increased twofold.[300]

In addition, depressed people who sought treatment for their disease through psychotherapy started to go to other, less-expensive counselors who promised patients quicker, easier help. This opened the door for clinical lay therapists, social workers and other professionals to hang out their shingles to help those with mental illnesses. "Some of these newer providers crassly advertised their wares with glaring boasts of 'Success in ten weeks—or your money back,' or 'obsessions and addictions—insurance accepted.'"[301]

**1990s: Managed Care Limits Access**
During the last decade of the twentieth century, many health insurance companies started the controversial practice of "managed care" (trying to control costs by covering treatments only from preselected doctors and only after patients obtained permission from the insurance companies to begin treatment). Managed care limited access to treatments for some depressed patients, but those who were able to obtain insurance coverage had access to many different options in psychotherapy counseling and antidepressant medications.

Unfortunately, mental health didn't fit well with managed services. "Ambiguous diagnoses and treatment regimens, combined with uncertain outcomes, left mental health at the mercy of the gatekeepers."[302] Psychotherapy, which tended to be a more expensive treatment for depression than medication, declined even more due to managed care's attempts to limit health-care costs. "Managed care effectively ended the viability of psychoanalysis as a treatment option for almost all Americans."[303]

What was worse was the tendency of managed care to pressure Americans into medication-only treatment, rather than the combination of psychotherapy and medicine. "Some patients responded by paying their therapists from their own funds, forcing them to negotiate more carefully over hourly rates and treatment durations. Therapists, in turn, learned to market their services partially on price, meaning that those who had charged less in the past were now increasingly attractive to prospective clients."[304]

The shift also led to many people thinking about depression treatment in terms of a chemical imbalance that should be corrected if possible with drugs. Basically, psychoanalysis fell out of favor, while psychopharmacology rose in prominence. "During the 1990s, psychiatrists and ordinary people alike learned to think of a wide variety of mental problems as chemical imbalances, and came to see chemical-balancing medications as the most sensible response. The shift transformed the practice of psychiatry, with analytic methods giving way to a focus on the pharmaceutical management of symptoms."[305]

A major new class of antidepressant medications emerged: selective serotonin reuptake inhibitor (SSRI) drugs. Prozac was the first of the SSRI medications in the late 1980s; others like Paxil, Zoloft, Celexa, Luvox, and Lexapro followed in the 1990s. "'Selective' meant that unlike earlier antidepressants, the drug targeted only serotonin, not serotonin and norepinephrine both. The selectivity was supposed to be a selling point, the idea being that a more targeted drug would cause fewer side effects."[306]

For my first depression treatments, my doctor put me on lithium and MAOIs. After starting a new medication, I went in twice a week to have my blood drawn so the doctor could check to see how much of the medication was in my bloodstream and how the drug was working.

Those older medications had many side effects, like constipation and dry mouth, but the one I remember the most was the craving for sweets. Many people with depression, especially women, didn't want to take those pills because they didn't want to gain weight. One time my craving for sweets was so strong, I ordered five gallons of ice cream from the local ice cream shop and went home to enjoy it over time.

Despite the popularity of antidepressants in the 1990s, many people with depression still pursued some form of psychotherapy—from well-trained professionals to lay counselors who hadn't gone through much training. "The majority of patients who sought mental-health care continued to be treated with psychotherapy alone, even though multiple studies showed that most people improved faster and more thoroughly when they were treated with both medication and therapy."[307]

"The other thing that starts coming out in the beginning of the 1990s is that while we now were viewing depression as this purely biologically caused event or genetically caused event, it turns out that, in fact, early life experiences really do play a certain role in some forms of depression," explains Dr. Scheftner. "So the perspective has really started to change to include a mixture of genetic and biology as well as early childhood events and trauma as influencing later-life experiences, emotions, and disease presentations like depression."

The 1990s featured a "proliferation of products and services and well-meaning educational efforts designed to help treat and prevent depression. For most commentators by the 1990s, depression was a major public health problem—and it had readily available consumer solutions, including medications and other kinds of methods to deal with unhappiness, such as 'learning vacations' to help people overcome loss or disappointment."[308]

As the twentieth century drew to a close, people suffering from depression had many different treatment options to consider. "Because it has become the accepted view that depression frequently has multiple causes, including biological, psychological and social causes, it has also become the norm that multiple professions and approaches to treatment have important roles to play in helping people overcome depression."[309]

PART III: THE TREATMENT

# CHAPTER FOURTEEN
## DEPRESSION TREATMENTS
## IN THE TWENTY-FIRST CENTURY

**"There's nothing, repeat, nothing to be ashamed of when you're going through a depression. If you get help, the chances of your licking it are really good. But you have to get yourself onto a safe path."**
—Mike Wallace, American television journalist

Thanks to recent scientific advances that allow more insight into the human brain and genetic makeup, medical professionals and depression patients alike are understanding depression in different ways. New depression treatments are emerging as well, so people suffering from depression have myriad potentially useful treatments to choose from as they navigate the journey toward healing. "It is very likely that future diagnostic systems will include the use of some genetic, brain-imaging, and biological markers of illness as they are discovered and correlated with characteristic symptoms, long-term course of illness, or drug responsiveness."[310]

Increased biological understanding is allowing researchers to develop a range of innovative approaches to depression in the twenty-first century. "New theories of depression are focusing on differences in neuron density in various regions of the brain; on the effect of stress on the birth and death of brain cells; on the alteration of feedback pathways in the brain and on the role of inflammation evoked by the stress response."[311]

Additionally, depressed people have begun to treat their disease in multiple ways rather than choosing one treatment, as many did in the past. This holistic approach to depression emphasizes the power of personal choice and that there are many different pathways to wellness. "Although people with depression usually have similar symptoms, everyone has a unique blend of personal history, current concerns, strengths, and preferences. Instead of a 'one-size-fits-all' approach, many people with depression, and their doctors and therapists, prefer an individualized, multifaceted plan."[312]

Here are some of treatment options currently available or in development.

**Genetic Tests**
The mapping of the human genetic code—the instruction book for human life—was a watershed moment in the twenty-first century. After Dr. Francis Collins and his team at the Human Genome Project successfully mapped all of the genes people can carry within their bodies, their accomplishment ushered in a new era of medicine. Genetic knowledge now makes it possible for researchers to look for genes that cause diseases like depression, and to develop treatments that treat diseases at the most fundamental level. Because different people carry different types of genes, new treatments for depression and other diseases that arise from genetic research can be personalized to each patient, potentially offering the maximum effectiveness for every individual.

However, the new field of genetic medicine hasn't yet progressed to the point where the specific genetic causes for depression are clearly understood. Nor are there currently any new depression treatments based on genetics that have been conclusively proven to be effective. Researchers all over the world are unraveling the biological pathways to depression, searching for clues that will help doctors and patients alike understand the causes and cures of depression. "If the genetic mechanisms [of depression] can be decoded, then new medications or other biological treatments could be designed to correct these abnormalities. Although the promise of genetic studies hasn't been realized yet, there are many good leads."[313]

What's known so far is that "inherited traits play a role in how antidepressants affect you. In some cases, where available, results of genetic tests (done by blood test or cheek swab) may offer clues about how your body will respond to a particular antidepressant."[314] However, no one has developed a "specific diagnostic biologic test for depression at this time."[315] There are several types of tests, such as the dexamethasone suppression test, PET, and SPECT functional brain-imaging scans, and genetic-marker tests, that can help diagnose depression. But as yet, nothing has been found to "accurately determine which patients need which forms of therapy."[316]

What researchers *can* say conclusively right now is that depression "originates in genetics and family inheritance. If one of your parents, brothers, or sisters has unipolar major depression, then you have a 20 percent chance of inheriting it yourself. If both of your parents have genes for depression, you have a 50 percent chance of getting it. However, even if no one in your family has unipolar major depression, the depressive genes can occur spontaneously on their own."[317]

For me, it was a revelation to learn that genetic depression ran in my family. My Uncle Norman, a psychiatrist who first diagnosed my depression, told me he had treated my grandfather, my grandfather's brothers, and my mother for the same disease. Not only did I have a name for this malaise, but I also wasn't alone in my struggle.

As I delved deeper into my family history of depression, I discovered its origins: my grandmother's side of the Folletts. All four of her sons had depression, although it was likely they called it by a different name in the early twentieth century. I can't tell you how many people in the Follett family in general had or have depression, but I do know others in the family suffered from the disease, my mother among them in her adult years.

Finding out if family members have suffered from depression can be enormously helpful to patients for a number of reasons. First, the patient knows he or she is not alone in battling this illness. Second, the patient realizes he or she wasn't responsible for contracting the disease—it was in their genes and thus unavoidable, much like other genetic diseases. Third, the patient can seek more targeted treatments.

Although there's a lack of new treatments based on genetics, some health-care providers use information from genetic tests to evaluate the effectiveness of older treatments, such as existing antidepressant drugs. For example, Dr. Deborah Serani, an American psychologist and expert on depression based in New York, New York, advises her own patients to take a genetic-testing panel called Cytochrome p450. This test can give the medical team valuable information to help them choose the most beneficial antidepressants and dosages for that specific patient. "The results gained from getting this test can minimize dangerous adverse drug interactions, side-step side effects, and offer greater confidence taking medication. ... It will significantly reduce the time and prolonged anguish of finding symptom relief by pinpointing which antidepressant medication, and what dosages, may be treatment productive."[318]

The Cytochrome p450 genetic-testing panel can help patients considering antidepressant drugs in two key ways—by identifying what a patient's genetic metabolism is for medications, and by revealing how other medications might affect the patient and alert a doctor to a potential adverse drug reaction.

**Brain Scans**

Brain-scan technology has improved and can be a useful tool for doctors and therapists in treatment decisions. "An explosion of research in recent years has helped us understand what happens in the major centers of brain activity when people become depressed."[319]

Brain scans have revealed that the cortex, or outer layer of the brain, is the part responsible for conscious thinking. Recent findings about the anatomy of depression reveal that the cortex "becomes *underactive* in many people with depression."[320] But the limbic areas—the ones responsible for emotions like anger, joy, sadness, and happiness—become *overactive* in many depressed people. Antidepressant medications first correct the limbic abnormalities. "Studies have found that CBT [cognitive behavioral therapy] has biological effects on the brain. CBT works first by improving functioning in the front of the cortex. Thus CBT appears to work from the 'top down,' and medication appears to work from the 'bottom up.'"[321]

Brain scans show how depression diagnosed through patient interviews affects the brain. Brain-imaging studies have demonstrated that the hippocampus—a memory-forming part of the brain—becomes injured if long periods of severe depression has been left untreated. The hippocampus actually responds to such damage by growing smaller. "Antidepressants, lithium, and the anticonvulsant Depakote appear to be protective and have been shown to cause the brain to synthesize growth factors for these neurons. In other words, it now appears that depression causes brain damage and treatment reverses this."[322]

Although such scans can show what the brains of depressed people look like after they have been diagnosed through medical interviews, the scans can't yet reliably help doctors diagnose depression in the first place. "There are no tests for the reduced serotonin of other neurochemicals involved in depression, because the amounts contained in the gaps between your brain cells are too tiny."[323]

Neurofeedback, often also called EEG biofeedback or brain-wave training, has been used to treat specific conditions, such as attention deficit hyperactivity disorder (ADHD) and epilepsy, but some scientific studies have found promising results in treating depression, among other conditions and diseases. Basically, "neurofeedback uses sensors to detect physical changes of the body ... [by] placing small sensors on the scalp to see changes in a person's [brain-wave] activity."[324] The treatment generally involves two or more sessions per week and has few negative side effects.

More research is being done to see how depression patients respond to neurofeedback training, but research has determined that it's an effective intervention for children with ADHD by improving impulse control and attentiveness, decreasing hyperactivity, raising intelligence scores, and improving academic performance. Qualified neurofeedback practitioners can be found through the International Society for Neurofeedback & Research in Miami, Florida.

**Electroconvulsive Therapy**

Another, more invasive treatment option for patients suffering from severe depression is electroconvulsive therapy (ECT). This treatment was used often during the early twentieth century but had detrimental side effects. Today it can be done without causing as many side effects. The treatment involves passing electrical currents through the brain while the patient is under anesthesia. ECT usually provides immediate relief from depression, especially in more severe cases that haven't responded to other treatments. "ECT is usually used for people who don't get better with medications, can't take antidepressants for health reasons, or are at high risk of suicide."[325]

ECT has a long history of being one of "the oldest and most effective treatment for severe, life-threatening depression, and modern anesthesia has eliminated most of the complications,"[326] except severe or long-term memory complaints. In the early days of ECT, the treatment was administered without any anesthesia or muscle-relaxing drugs, leading many patients to experience fear, pain, and seizures during the procedure. However, during the twenty-first century, medical teams use anesthesia and take precautions to guard against seizures.

Although ECT is quite effective at alleviating the symptoms of depression—it has a remission rate (a decrease or disappearance of symptoms) ranging from 55 to 86 percent[327]—it's still reserved only for the most severe cases of depression. "ECT … is used when a very rapid response is potentially life-saving—for example, when a patient is lying in bed all day, refusing to eat or dress herself, having hallucinations or delusions of sin, guilt, or punishment, and talking of wanting to be dead."[328] (See Chapter 16 for more on ECT.)

**Magnetic Stimulation**

A new way of stimulating the brain to try to relieve depression is through transcranial magnetic stimulation (TMS), which is also called repetitive transcranial magnetic stimulation (rTMS). TMS was approved by the FDA in 2008 as a treatment for depression that hasn't improved through traditional treatments like antidepressant medications.

TMS sends a series of magnetic pulses targeted toward brain cells the medical team seeks to stimulate. Patients remain completely conscious during TMS treatments. The treatment generally takes place while the patient reclines in a chair with a treatment coil applied to his or her scalp. Brief magnetic pulses are sent through the coil to invigorate nerve cells in the brain that regulate mood and depression. Usually, the treatment cycle runs five times a week for up to six weeks.[329]

Some doctors view TMS as a better alternative to ECT because it doesn't use anesthesia or include the risk of seizures.[330] However, the potential of TMS as a depression treatment has yet to be fully explored. "Like any very new technique, the details of how best to use it are still being explored; placement of the magnetic coils, stimulus parameters, frequency and duration of treatment, and efficacy are still being evaluated. Generally, improved outcome occurs with greater course duration, pulse intensity, and quantity."[331]

Some experts have advocated a more cautious approach to TMS. "While rTMS has been approved by the FDA for use in treatment-resistant depression, you may want to wait for more information on rTMS."[332]

**Vagus Nerve Stimulation**

Another new depression treatment that focuses on stimulating the human brain to alleviate depression is vagus nerve stimulation (VNS). This procedure was approved by the FDA in 2005 for depression that hasn't responded to other treatments. It involves a doctor surgically inserting an electrical device similar to a pacemaker in a patient's chest, connecting it to wires, and wrapping those wires around the vagus nerve that runs through the chest and connects to the brain.

One major drawback is that VNS works at a snail's pace compared with both antidepressant drugs and ECT. "It is not unusual to wait three to six months or more to see some response."[333] But the procedure has proven effective for some patients. "A two-year outcome study of 59 treatment-resistant depression patients receiving VNS reported one- and two-year response rates of 44 percent and 42 percent; impressively, 81 percent of patients were still receiving VNS at two years."[334]

VNS has been a useful tool for relieving depression in some patients who have suffered severe forms of the disease, but the risky procedure should be carefully considered before trying. "Despite its potential usefulness, VNS has many safety issues and is currently a rather drastic procedure for the treatment of unipolar major depression. Surgically opening your chest is a serious procedure that leaves you vulnerable to infection, and we do not yet know enough about the long-term effects of VNS on your vagus nerve or your health in general."[335]

**Antidepressant Medications**
The main classes of medications invented in the twentieth century—tricyclics, MAOIs, and SSRIs—are still in common use today. Today, SSRIs are the most commonly prescribed of all the antidepressant medications. The medical profession often starts with an SSRI prescription because those "medications are safer and generally cause fewer side effects than other types of antidepressants. SSRIs include fluoxetine (Prozac), paroxetine (Paxil, Pexeva), sertraline (Zoloft), citalopram (Celexa), and escitalopram (Lexapro)."[336]

SSRIs in general lower aggression, anxiety, and depression, while upping appetite and weight gain. Also, these medications can have a detrimental impact on a patient's sex drive. "Serotonin antidepressants usually prolong the time to reach orgasm. Most modern antidepressants have a strong serotonin effect. Norepinephrine generally increases physical energy, motivation, and anxiety, while decreasing appetite, weight, and sleep. Dopamine tends to increase alertness, concentration, and optimism, while decreasing appetite."[337]

People who use antidepressants usually experience some success if they stick with their treatment plans, but there is still the persistent problem of some patients stopping antidepressant treatments prematurely. The key to successfully using antidepressant medications is having the right attitude about the treatment plan.

The patient's attitude towards medication during the first weeks of treatment is of paramount importance. If family members, patients, and doctors all agree that drugs are a necessary part of treatment, the chance of success is high. But if the patient or those in his support group view antidepressants as a crutch, a weakness, or unnatural, chances of long-term recovery diminish. "Similarly, if the therapist views medication as a powerful partner to psychotherapy, this attitude will strengthen the treatment plan, whereas the belief that beginning medication means the therapy is failing can be harmful."[338]

In June 2017, the U.S. Army announced it had commissioned a study on whether injecting an anesthetic into the neck would alleviate symptoms of post-traumatic stress disorder (PTSD), which soldiers often experience along with depression. "The $2 million Army study constitutes the first large-scale randomized control research into the use of shots—called stellate ganglion blocks—to treat PTSD. The injections have been used for decades for arm pain and shingles."[339] Doctors in favor of the treatment emphasize that the shots don't cure the disorder but merely "eases [PTSD] enough to allow talk therapy, pharmaceuticals and other approaches to achieve long-term improvements."[340]

**Antidepressants and Placebos**

A headline-making 2008 research study (called "Initial Severity and Antidepressant Benefits: A Meta-Analysis of Data Submitted to the Food and Drug Administration") shows that placebos were just as effective against depression as antidepressant medications taken by patients in the study. The American, British, and Canadian doctors who conducted the study evaluated the placebo pills' effectiveness against that of all types of antidepressant drugs, such as tricyclics, MAOIs, and SSRIs.

The analysis conducted by the researchers of both the published and unpublished data from drug companies found that most of the benefits from antidepressants could be attributed to the placebo effect. The study's lead researcher, Dr. Irving Kirsch, explains in an article he wrote called "Antidepressants and the Placebo Effect" for the German medical psychology journal *Zeitschrift fur Psychologie* that "some antidepressants increase serotonin levels, some decrease it, and some have no effect at all on serotonin. Nevertheless, they all show the same therapeutic benefit. Even the small statistical difference between antidepressants and placebos may be an enhanced placebo effect, due to the fact that most patients and doctors in clinical trials successfully break blind."[341]

Dr. Kirsch described antidepressant medications as "the riskiest and most harmful"[342] of all possible depression treatments, stating, "If they are to be used at all, it should be as a last resort, when depression is extremely severe and all other treatment alternatives have been tried and failed."[343] (See Chapters 16, 17, and 18 for more information on different treatment options.)

### Combining Antidepressants and Therapy

Today more depressed people are opting for a combination of medication and psychotherapy, and research backs up the benefits of utilizing these two treatment options.

"Psychotherapists have long argued with psychopharmacologists that depressive symptoms motivate introspection, self-awareness, struggle, growth, and change. Psychopharmacologists have argued that relief of human suffering through the use of medications is worthwhile and sometimes even life-saving. Fortunately, the psychotherapists and psychopharmacologists are gradually declaring a truce in this turf war, recognizing that collaboration and use of all appropriate treatment modalities allows the best treatment of both mind and brain."[344]

The scientific evidence proves that using both treatments can boost success. "More than thirty years of studies on medication and psychotherapy for depression have found that combining the two treatments can provide a greater overall treatment benefit than receiving medication or psychotherapy alone."[345]

### Psychotherapy

Psychotherapy in the twenty-first century offers more avenues for depression treatment. Patients are now able to seek therapy not only from medical doctors (psychiatrists), but also from less-expensive practitioners, such as psychologists, licensed clinical social workers, clergy, lay counselors, and support groups.

According to the Mayo Clinic, two current types of therapy—

cognitive behavioral therapy and interpersonal therapy—are especially effective for treating depression. Cognitive behavioral therapy helps depressed people understand how they are thinking and behaving in unhealthy ways, and helps them change those thoughts and behaviors to healthier ones. Interpersonal therapy helps patients study the significant relationships in their lives, then improve communication and learn from those relationships to alleviate their depression.

Here are some other types of therapy available for depressed people:

- **Psychoeducation (PE)** teaches patients about unipolar major depression, including the causes of it and how to alleviate the depression. Numerous studies have shown that PE has a good track record as a psychotherapy that relieves depression.[346]
- **Psychodynamic Psychotherapy (PP)** has its roots in Jungian and Freudian psychoanalysis. It assists the patient with learning about his or her inner self as a tool to treat depression. Although a slow process, PP has the potential to provide patients with lasting recovery from unipolar major depression. "Modern psychodynamic psychotherapy uses the interaction between psychotherapist and client as a tool to reveal internal assumptions and fantasies."[347]
- **Supportive Therapy (ST)** has as its goal encouragement, reassurance, and nurturance through positive social feedback. ST reassures the patient that things are not as bad as he or she thinks and that success is right around the corner. "Unfortunately, from the depths of depression, this rosy view is often annoying ... ST can make you feel good for a while, but it might not help you make the changes that you need in your life."[348]

## Stress Management

The newest approaches to understanding and treating depression also emphasize the importance of managing stress. Depression genes make the brain overreact to stress, which can cascade into a domino effect. When stressed, each of us secretes steroid stress hormones and excitatory neurochemicals in our brains, but those with unipolar major depression can't shut off the secretion after the stressful period ends.

Stress chemicals on high alert for long periods of time can damage and kill brain cells, which can trigger a unipolar major depression. "Moreover, after an episode of unipolar major depression begins, it also provokes the secretion of stress steroid hormones and excitatory neurochemicals. Thus, depression causes a stress reaction that builds on itself."[349]

This new focus on the role that stress plays in depression means that "depression treatments on the horizon include ... long-term cognitive behavioral therapy for stress management,"[350] as well as "anti-inflammatory drugs"[351] to reduce inflammation in people's brains and elsewhere in their bodies. (See Chapter 19 on how exercise can help with stress relief in depression patients.)

### Digital Therapy

A growing number of health providers have begun using digital therapy, such as web-based courses and mobile apps, to help those who suffer from depression. "Research ... suggests that digital therapies augmented by coaches who are available by text or phone can be as effective as evidence-based traditional therapy in treating some people with depression."[352]

In the early 2000s, clinical psychologists started putting digital interventions for depression online. But those first efforts have evolved from essentially PowerPoint presentations to more interactive and personalized mobile apps, such as Lantern, Ginger.io, and Joyable. "They typically ask users to enter information about their moods and behaviors, then offer problem-solving suggestions, prompts to help patients retrain responses from negative situations, and daily health tips."[353]

Dr. Stephen Schueller, an assistant professor of preventive medicine at Northwestern University in Evanston, Illinois, views digital therapies as continuing to evolve into a more effective depression treatment option. "The future is trying to better understand how to make these apps and sites engaging," he says.[354]

One of the biggest hurdles in getting depressed patients to try these digital therapy options is knowing which ones are trustworthy. The

PsyberGuide website headed by Dr. Schueller gives users a standardized rating system to assist in selecting products or apps for a variety of mental-health concerns.

Another way mental health professionals are tapping into technology has been through the information captured by smartphones. "Our smartphones measure our movements with accelerometers, our location with GPS and our social engagement with the number of calls and texts we send," writes Dr. Daniel Barron in an April 2021 *Wall Street Journal* article. "These data have extraordinary potential for psychiatric diagnosis and treatment. Studies have shown that the words we use to express ourselves on Facebook and Twitter can predict the emergence of conditions like postpartum depression and psychosis. A person's recent Google search history, it turns out, is a better predictor of suicide than their clinician's most recent notes."[355]

Dr. Barron sees these digital tools as complements to assist psychiatrists in measuring a patient's in-session behavior. "Each visit to a therapist creates a wealth of clinical data that is currently wasted because it's not recorded or analyzed," he writes. The psychiatrist and medical director of the Interventional Pain Psychiatry Program at Brigham and Women's Hospital in Boston, Massachusetts, recommends doctors in his field embrace technologies such as speech and facial recognition to "measure a patient's expression, the words they use and the intonation of their voice. Such tools could be used to recognize the subtle changes that occur when a patient is about to become floridly manic, or to analyze how they respond to treatment." [356]

Two treatment models based on data analysis have emerged. One model has doctors calibrating laboratory tests and discussing with patients what data might be helpful in their treatment and how to collect it. This approach gives patients more autonomy over whether or how much data to share with their medical providers. The second model involves a "consumer-facing product similar to the genetic testing offered by 23andMe, in which people pay for access to their own data and then decide who to share it with."[357]

However these treatment models evolve, "using big data to make psychiatry more precise and effective has the potential to help all patients," Dr. Barron concludes.[358]

During the first part of the twenty-first century, doctors and scientists have gained fresh insight into how depression works and how new therapies and treatment combat the disease. With continued advancements in this area, patients with depression no longer have to fear the illness, but can face it with more confidence that relief is attainable.

## Stress-Reduction Techniques

Here are some examples of stress-reduction techniques that depressed people may find beneficial:

- Acupuncture
- Relaxation techniques and exercises, such as yoga or tai chi
- Meditation
- Guided imagery
- Massage therapy
- Music or art therapy
- Spirituality
- Aerobic exercise

Experts advise patients not to rely solely on these therapies to treat depression, but to use such stress-management techniques alongside medication and psychotherapy.[359]

PART III: THE TREATMENT

# CHAPTER FIFTEEN
## DEPRESSION TREATMENTS
## OF THE NEAR FUTURE

**"Depression is like a bruise that never goes away. A bruise in your mind. You just got to be careful not to touch it where it hurts. It's always there though."**
—Jeffrey Eugenides, American novelist and short story writer

Despite the increased awareness and options for treatment, many depressed people still can't find the help they need. "About 30 percent of all people with depression don't respond adequately to the available treatments. ... That's a dismal failure rate,"[360] according to a 2017 *Time* article.

The good news is that several promising new depression treatments have recently been approved and others are on the horizon. These newcomers include mental-health apps for counseling; the ketamine hydrochloride drug, Spravato/esketamine, and Zulresso/brexanolone; gene therapy; and holistic medicine. These advancements reflect a more targeted approach increasingly being used by health-care providers when treating depression. "Scientists are gaining a more nuanced picture of what depression is—not a monolithic disease, but probably dozens of distinct maladies—and they're getting closer to learning what works for which kind of ailment."[361]

"As we ease into the second decade of the twenty-first century, we've started to look beyond medication into different areas of depression treatments," says Dr. Robert Shulman,[362] acting director of Rush University Medical Group in Chicago, Illinois. "There's been more out-of-the-box thinking about what's going on with depression outside of medication. We're learning more and more about how a disease affects the entire person, and that's leading to more innovative and successful treatments for depression and other mental-health diseases."

## Ketamine

Since the 1960s, ketamine has been an emergency-room staple for helping to ease the pain of children brought in with dislocated shoulders and broken bones. Because of its fast-numbing properties, burn centers and veterinarians also use the drug. In addition, it is known as a popular party drug dubbed "Special K." But most people may not know it can be used to treat depression. "Since 2006, dozens of studies have reported that it can also reverse the kind of severe depression that traditional antidepressants often don't touch."[363] Ketamine is drawing attention for its results in patients with treatment-resistant depression and its apparent ability to work much faster than traditional antidepressants.

That breakthrough is pushing the American Psychiatric Association toward a tacit endorsement of ketamine for treatment-resistant depression. "Experts are calling it the most significant advance in mental health in more than half a century. They point to studies showing ketamine not only produces a rapid and robust antidepressant effect; it also puts a quick end to suicidal thinking."[364]

The U.S. Food and Drug Administration (FDA) hasn't yet approved ketamine for use as an antidepressant, but anesthesiologists have been using ketamine since 1970 in large doses to put people to sleep before surgery, and clinical studies on using it to treat depression are eliciting excitement from both doctors and patients. "'It's been a paradigm shift, that now we can achieve rapid antidepressant effects,' says Dr. Carlos Zarate, chief of the experimental therapeutics and pathophysiology branch at the National Institute of Mental Health in Bethesda, Maryland, and one of the foremost researchers of ketamine's use in treating depression. 'Now we know there's something radically different.'"[365]

As evidence mounts of ketamine's effectiveness in treating depression, full FDA approval may be coming soon that will allow for it to be prescribed freely as an antidepressant. In addition, an increasing number of academic medical centers, including the Cleveland Clinic, the Mayo Clinic, the University of California at San Diego, and Yale University, are now prescribing ketamine for severe depression. One San Francisco psychiatrist dubbed ketamine "the next big thing," noting the long-term success rate of many of her own patients.

A RollingStone.com article about ketamine reports on that ketamine seems to be on the fast track to approval: "The FDA has yet to give ketamine the green light for treatment as an antidepressant, which means anyone using the substance is doing it off-label and footing the bill. ... The FDA granted intranasal esketamine a breakthrough therapy designation twice in the last four years—first in November 2013 for treatment-resistant depression, then again in August 2016 for severe depression with imminent risk of suicide. The designation helps speed up development of the ketamine-based drug, which is undergoing a phase III trial. ... According to the National Institutes of Health, more than ninety clinical trials studying ketamine's antidepressant properties are either underway or have completed."[366]

Currently, ketamine is only approved for use as an anesthetic by the FDA. At least one drug company, Janssen Pharmaceutica, is conducting tests on esketamine, a nasal spray form that could be used to treat depression. Janssen planned to submit the nasal spray to the FDA for approval by 2019.[367] The agency has, however, "designated esketamine a 'break-through therapy,' which means it can speed through the typically lengthy drug development process and get to market more quickly.[368]

Exactly how ketamine works to treat depression is still unclear, but studies have found that ketamine can reduce functional connectivity of the subgenual anterior cingulate cortex, a collar-like region near the front of the brain that's connected to the prefrontal and frontal cortexes. The unique position of the anterior cingulate cortex allows it to control emotion, impulse control, decision-making, and reward anticipation.

Research suggests ketamine decreases "the 'over-wiredness' of the emotional regulation area. ... In other words: Severely depressed people on ketamine may feel relief from repetitive thoughts of worthlessness and inadequacy."[369]

A Webmd.com article on ketamine noted that "in a handful of ketamine clinics around the country, people who weren't helped by standard treatments are getting a series of infusions to ease their depression. The drug has also been used in emergency rooms for curbing suicidal thoughts, making it a potential lifesaver. ... Ketamine acts quickly—often within hours or less—and health care professionals who give it to patients at therapeutic doses say it has mild and brief side effects in most people. But it hasn't been thoroughly studied for long-term safety and effectiveness."[370]

Ketamine shows exciting promise as a depression treatment, but doctors caution that patients shouldn't view ketamine as a magic solution to all of their depression problems. Psychiatrist Dr. Alan Manevitz said in the Webmd.com article that "ketamine is not a miracle drug at all. It may momentarily take them away from that catastrophic place they're in with depression, but you're not addressing the rest of the patient. It's a complex issue to treat psychiatric issues, and you have to treat the whole patient."[371]

Medical professionals and patients also must bear in mind that ketamine can be addictive. More research can help determine the optimal doses for treating depression without causing addiction. "The positive results so far don't mean a person with severe depression should use ketamine as a treatment tool outside of a clinical setting. Ketamine has addictive properties, so there is some risk for long-term substance abuse."[372]

Time will tell if ketamine can be a meaningful tool in treating depression. "Earlier this year, the APA [American Psychological Association] task force released a consensus statement in *JAMA Psychiatry* that acknowledged ketamine's effects on depression and other mood disorders, but also noted its limited data concerning its effectiveness and safety. ... It's potentially one of the most interesting new treatments to be developed in the treatment of depression in decades and it holds great promise, ... but we have to keep our eyes open to the potential risk and the fact that we still really aren't sure how to use this drug in the long-term."[373]

## Spravato/Esketamine

Spravato (brand name)/esketamine (generic name), which the FDA approved in March 2019, is a nasal spray derived from ketamine that is "the first truly new medication for major depression in decades."[374] This new medication is showing significantly promising results so far. "In one study, 70 percent of patients with treatment-resistant depression who were started on an oral antidepressant and intranasal esketamine improved, compared to just over half in the group that did not receive the medication (called the placebo group)."[375]

In a *Yale Medicine* article, Dr. John Krystal, chief psychiatrist at Yale Medicine in New Haven, Connecticut, calls Spravato/esketamine "a game changer," adding: "When you take ketamine, it triggers reactions in your cortex that enable brain connections to regrow. It's the reaction to ketamine, not the presence of ketamine in the body, that constitutes its effects." The article notes, "'this is exactly what makes ketamine unique as an antidepressant,' says Dr. Krystal. ... Interestingly, studies from Yale research labs showed that the drug ketamine, which was widely used as anesthesia during surgeries, triggers glutamate production, which, in a complex, cascading series of events, prompts the brain to form new neural connections. This makes the brain more adaptable and able to create new pathways, and gives patients the opportunity to develop more positive thoughts and behaviors. This was an effect that had not been seen before, even with traditional antidepressants."[376]

Esketamine has a different impact on the brain than other antidepressants, including SSRIs, according to researchers. "The antidepressant esketamine affects a different system within the brain: the glutamatergic system, which is important for processing information. People with depression often don't have as many connections, or synapses, between brain cells, which may contribute to an increase in symptoms of depression. Esketamine helps create more of those connections between the brain cells."[377]

The creation or repair of brain-cell connections by esketamine may help alleviate some depression symptoms, including decreasing thoughts of suicide faster than other antidepressants. Because esketamine can be administered via nasal spray, it enters the bloodstream faster than pills or other oral medications. "That swift delivery of the medication to the brain results in depression symptoms beginning to ease within several hours, and many people report feeling significant relief within one day."[378]

In an article for the National Institute of Mental Health, Dr. Joshua Gordon says Spravato/esketamine is a "remarkable new medication … which targets treatment-resistant depression (TRD),"[379] citing the drug's ability to rapidly relieve depressive symptoms. However, despite the promising results so far, Dr. Gordon cautions that neither ketamine nor Spravato/esketamine are magical solutions for depression. "Ketamine and esketamine work, but both have significant drawbacks," he noted. "Many patients experience uncomfortable dissociative symptoms, hypertension, or other side effects for a few hours after administration. Because of these symptoms, as well as the potential for abuse, both need to be administered in a doctor's office."[380]

Questions about the long-term efficacy and side effects of the drugs have yet to be fully answered, but studies are ongoing. As Dr. Gordon says, "[T]he discovery of the rapid antidepressant capabilities of ketamine has paved the way to asking them questions we couldn't even have dreamed of back in the 1990s, questions we're only asking because of an educated guess."[381]

Spravato/esketamine may be one option to consider in conjunction with other methods in an overall treatment plan for depression patients. "To date, it has only been shown to be effective when taken in combination with an oral antidepressant. For these reasons, esketamine is not considered a first-line treatment option for depression. It's only prescribed for people with moderate to severe major depressive disorder who haven't been helped by at least two other depression medications. In the end, though, the FDA approval of esketamine gives doctors another valuable tool in their arsenal against depression."[382]

For now, Spravato/esketamine offers hope to those who haven't found relief through other treatments. "For the right type of patient, there is great promise that esketamine can offer help for depression and lower the risk of suicide where other treatment options have failed."[383]

## Zulresso (Brexanolone)

The FDA approved another depression medication in March 2019 calling it a "breakthrough therapy": Zulresso (brand name)/brexanolone (generic name). Zulresso/brexanolone is the first-ever drug approved in the United States to treat postpartum depression, a condition that can affect women after they've given birth. Zulresso/brexanolone is "a revolutionary new medication that acts to rapidly reduce symptoms and restore function to those struggling with the devastating effects of postpartum depression."[384]

Postpartum depression is a serious condition that can be life-threatening when severe and can interfere with the maternal-infant bond. Women suffering from postpartum depression often experience thoughts of self-harm or harming their child. "This approval marks the first time a drug has been specifically approved to treat postpartum depression, providing an important new treatment option," says Dr. Tiffany Farchione, acting director of the Division of Psychiatry Products in the FDA's Center for Drug Evaluation and Research, in a press release announcing the approval. "Because of concerns about serious risks, including excessive sedation or sudden loss of consciousness during administration, Zulresso has been approved with a Risk Evaluation and Mitigation Strategy (REMS) and is only available to patients through a restricted distribution program at certified health-care facilities where the health-care provider can carefully monitor the patient."[385]

Some have labeled Zulresso/brexanolone "the vanguard of a new wave of antidepressants."[386] This fast-acting drug also has fewer side effects than similar medications. However, what makes Zulresso/ brexanolone and Spravato/esketamine so different is the way researchers approached development by focusing on how the different neural circuits work with brain function. "The purpose of the brain is as a communication network,"[387] says Jim Doherty, chief research officer at Sage Therapeutics in Cambridge, Massachusetts, which manufacturers Zulresso. Rather than thinking merely about receptors and drug molecules, "we try to think as much as we can at that level [of the whole communication network] to understand what are going to be the circuit-level consequences of our molecules."[388]

## Mental-Health Apps

Technological advances in artificial intelligence (AI) have made counseling treatment more accessible and convenient for people suffering from depression. The artificial intelligence that is programmed into today's mental-health apps makes it easier for people to treat their depression when traditional counseling isn't a viable option. Now, all depression patients need to do is open an app to begin treatment, rather than dealing with the time-consuming and expensive logistics of meeting with a counselor in person. "AI and machine learning have the potential to revolutionize the way we diagnose and treat mental-health conditions. In the future, algorithms may be our first line of defense against the mental-health struggles that can be debilitating for so many people."[389]

Artificial Intelligence apps can provide 24/7 accessibility at a low cost. "With a preference for convenience and instant feedback, artificial intelligence ... is gaining ground with patients in mental and behavioral health care."[390] App programs gather data from users that is used to create relevant responses, with the engagement level changing as more data is collected. "Through this process, the app is able to better detect and work toward meeting a user's individual behavioral- and emotional-health goals and needs."[391]

One of the appeals of these apps is that programs using AI can be accessed anonymously, thus preserving privacy. Another plus is the removal of barriers to treatment for mental-health issues, such as a dearth of service providers in certain areas. Mental-health apps and programs created by AI provide access via laptop, tablet, or smartphone at any time of day or night. "Compared to the cost of therapy fees, as well as accounting for missed work, commuting, and other needs, these apps are also low- to no-cost alternatives."[392]

The option to talk with a chatbot may have an appeal for certain app users. "[S]ome people may feel more comfortable sharing their struggles with an anonymous chatbot than a human being. ... [C]hatbots and other app-based tools for tracking and improving mood could be hugely beneficial, particularly for patients who would otherwise have trouble accessing care. There are already multiple smartphone-based tools that can walk patients through exercises based on cognitive behavioral therapy and other research-backed techniques for coping with symptoms. A chatbot could be a lifeline for a patient who's struggling in the middle of the night."[393]

Despite the benefits of AI-based counseling, it is limited in what it can provide compared with in-person counseling from professional human counselors. Apps are not supposed to take the place of clinical treatment of mental-health conditions, such as depression, but to be used in conjunction with in-person counseling. These apps can provide a helpful tool, such as reducing bias and human error, and by flagging early warning signs of trouble. "Algorithms have already been proven to be successful at detecting signs of conditions like depression and post-traumatic stress disorder by analyzing speech patterns and facial expressions. Mental- and physical-health providers could use these tools during patient intake meetings to serve as a backup."[394]

Apps can also flag symptoms busy medical professionals or counselors might otherwise miss or gloss over. "Imagine if your smartphone could alert your doctor that you're at risk of depression based on how fast you're typing or how often you're leaving your house. In one study, algorithms using language analysis were 100 [percent] accurate at identifying teens who were likely to develop psychosis. These tools already exist, and they're incredibly powerful. ... Timely interventions are crucial in many areas of mental health, especially in the field of medication dependence. AI tools can provide invaluable support to human providers and patients between appointments, creating daily checkpoints that can catch a downturn before it turns into a dangerous spiral."[395]

## Gene Therapy
Another depression treatment that looks promising for the future is gene

therapy. Now in the experimental stage, gene therapy pinpoints specific genes that contribute to depression in individual patients and aims to change those genes in ways that relieve depression. (See the genetic tests section on page 134 for more on hereditary depression.)

Some people with depression could have maladaptive genes that affect arousal, hormone levels, neural activation, neurotransmission, and personality development. "In the future, it is thought that gene therapy could allow medical professionals to treat depression via modification (insertion) of a specific gene. In theory, this would target maladaptive genes that contribute to depression, and correct them via insertion of the more favorable genes. The technique of gene therapy uses a vector (most often viral) to transport a gene to specific cells where the gene is required. After the gene has been successfully inserted, the gene is processed by the cells, and proteins are manufactured. The manufactured proteins then follow specific orders (as dictated by their programming) within cells."[396]

In 2016, a major breakthrough happened while researching gene therapy as a depression treatment. A research study of nearly 460,000 people (conducted by scientists from Massachusetts General Hospital, Pfizer Pharmaceuticals, and the commercial genetic testing company 23andMe) found "no fewer than fifteen discrete regions on the human genome associated with the development of major depressive disorder (MDD). ... If depression is a breakdown in the operating system that is the human brain, the new study may have pinpointed the bad lines of code responsible."[397] Investigators for the large study used genetic information from some people who had seen a doctor for symptoms of depression, but they also used data from other people who had never done so.

It is unclear what the researchers will do with this data. "In the short term, it might be possible to use the new information to refine the existing way depression is treated—developing more finely targeted drugs to adjust neurotransmitters in more precisely targeted ways, say. But the more ambitious goal is to try to stop depression before it even gets to the point that it needs to be treated. That could mean identifying at-risk people long before the onset of the disease and pharmaceutically targeting the proteins that the anomalous genes produce."[398]

One of the study's authors, Dr. Roy Perlis, director of the Center for Experimental Drugs and Diagnostics at Massachusetts General Hospital in Boston, Massachusetts, said that identifying the 15 genetic regions that are linked to depression can pave the way for the development of new, personalized medicine treatments for the disease. "Understanding what these depression genes do in the body makes it easier for scientists to find new drugs and interventions that have the opposite effect, which will make the search for treatments ever more precise. 'It essentially gives us a target to aim at,' Perlis says."[399]

Gene therapy is proving to be effective on rodents, and researchers think it may have multiple uses in treating humans with depression. "There are a variety of therapeutic targets to be considered in depression. Many of these genetic biomarkers already have been documented as targets for novel antidepressant drugs. … While gene therapy hasn't yet been studied in humans for the treatment of depression, preliminary rodent studies highlight its efficacy."[400]

A University of Cambridge study of marmoset monkeys "suggests that individual variation in genes alters our ability to regulate emotions, providing new insights that could help in the development of personalized therapies to tackle anxiety and depression."[401] As one of the researchers involved in the U.K. study said, "Our research suggests that differences in our DNA may help predict which of us will respond well to these medicines and which of us require a different approach. This could be assessed using genetic testing."[402]

Another study, from Georgia's Augusta University on mice, revealed that activating a certain gene "boosts the activity of certain neurons involved in depression can reverse symptoms of the condition in male mice."[403] A focus on a single gene discovered that a "variant of a protein-encoding gene known as Sirtuin1 (SIRT1) correlates with a much higher risk of depression. Now, new research finds that direct activation of this gene in the prefrontal cortex—a brain area we associate with complex thinking and planning of socially-appropriate responses—can reverse symptoms of depression in male mice." The study's author plans further investigation into whether existing drugs "affect SIRT1 in a similar way to the activator they used in this research. The scientists theorize that we may one day use SIRT1 activators as an effective treatment for major depression."[404]

Gene-therapy research into possible genetic treatments for depression is continuing to progress. Although no specific genetic treatments are yet available for human depression, researchers continue to explore the potential with the hope of creating gene-therapy treatments that will improve patients' quality of life.

### Future Medications

Medical researchers increasingly are exploring how to use medication to treat depression in different ways than in the past. For example, scientists in the United Kingdom believe that "depression could be treated using anti-inflammatory drugs ... after determining that it is a physical illness caused by a faulty immune system."[405]

In 2016, the U.K.'s National Health Service filled more than 64 million antidepressant prescriptions, a two-fold increase in ten years. "Current treatment is largely centered around restoring mood-boosting chemicals in the brain, such as serotonin, but experts now think an overactive immune system triggers inflammation throughout the entire body, sparking feelings of hopelessness, unhappiness, and fatigue."[406]

Recent papers and clinical trials have supported the finding that by treating inflammation, depressive symptoms abate. "The immune system triggers an inflammatory response when it feels it is under threat, sparking wide-ranging changes in the body such as increasing red blood cells, in anticipation that it may need to heal a wound soon. ... But recent studies have shown that nerve cells in the brain are linked to immune function and one can have an impact on the other."[407]

As Sir Robert Lechler, president of London's Academy of Medical Sciences, says, "You can't separate the mind from the body. ... The immune system does produce behavior. You're not just a little bit miserable if you've got a long-term condition, there is a real mechanistic connection between the mind, the nervous system, and the immune system."[408] This connection might lead to a new field that would study the link between the immune system and neurology.

Another interesting approach would enable at-risk patients to take a preventive pill to ward off depression. This particular concept is a byproduct of efforts by doctors to prevent depression in head- and neck-cancer patients, who are partially vulnerable to developing depression while undergoing cancer treatment. A group of researchers looked at "what would happen if non-depressed patients were given antidepressants before receiving treatment for head and neck cancer. ... Patients taking an antidepressant were 60 percent less likely to experience depression compared with peers who were given a placebo."[409]

This anticipatory approach has shown promise with other high-risk patients as well, including those suffering from hepatitis C, strokes, and melanoma. "These findings provide compelling reasons for physicians and patients to consider using these medicines to preempt mental-health issues."[410] But this approach has its drawbacks, especially relating to the lack of implementation guidelines. It's also "not clear how long patients should stay on these medications or at what level of risk someone warrants prophylaxis [preventative] antidepressants."[411]

Another consideration is how the patient would handle the side effects of antidepressants, which could impact other medical treatments. In addition, critics have wondered "about the financial incentives behind those who are promoting prophylactic antidepressants," given that at least one study had the lead author on the payroll of a pharmaceutical company that manufactured the antidepressant used.[412]

Another consideration is that "[e]xpanding the use of antidepressants to people who have never had depression could substantially increase national consumption of psychiatric medications."[413] However, these recent studies do suggest that "doctors may be able to prepare patients for challenging situations in ways that protect them from sliding into clinical depression. Some patients may benefit from early use of antidepressants, others with therapy or a combination of the two."[414]

## Microbes and Depression

Can bacteria in our guts help in the fight against depression? In some cases, the answer may be yes. Although "the notion that the state of our gut governs our state of mind dates back more than 100 years,"[415] it's only been recently that scientists have revisited that connection. Today, gut bacteria has become the unlikely hero in our quest for better health, with probiotics being added to numerous foods, such as yogurts, and holistic practitioners touting the healing properties of microbes.

In recent years, researchers have begun studying the relationship between gut bacteria and depression, finding "tantalizing hints about how the bacteria in the gut can alter the way the brain works."[416] Preliminary research on lab mice have shown that having "the right bacteria in your gut could brighten mood and perhaps even combat pernicious mental disorders including anxiety and depression."[417]

The gut-brain connection appears to go both ways—"the brain acts on gastrointestinal and immune functions that help to shape the gut's microbial makeup, and gut microbes make neuroactive compounds, including neurotransmitters and metabolites that also act on the brain."[418] In studies conducted on mice, researchers found interesting relationships between good gut bacteria and good mental health. One Japanese study from more than ten years ago "showed for the first time that intestinal microbes could influence stress responses in the brain and hinted at the possibility of using probiotic treatments to affect brain function in beneficial ways."[419] Other research appears to confirm that "our guts play a role in our emotions and perhaps even our behavior."[420]

It's early days in gut-brain research, "but so far, the results are compelling. … [Scientists] are amassing evidence that they hope will lead to 'psychobiotics'—bacteria-based drugs made out of live organisms that could improve mental health."[421]

Experts continue to test gut bacteria as potential future therapies for depression, with "mounting evidence suggest[ing] that intestinal microbes profoundly shape our thinking and behavior. Human trials are now underway to investigate how these microbes boost our overall well-being. If the results hold up, new bacteria-based therapies could expand a mental-health treatment landscape that has been mostly stagnant for decades."[422]

Many of our bacterial genes assist in building molecules that digest food, keep harmful microbes at arm's length, and influence how we process emotions. "For starters, the bacteria in your gut produce about 90 percent of the serotonin in your body—yep, the same happy hormone that regulates your moods and promotes well-being."[423]

Microbes in the gut can affect the brain in surprising ways. "Some bacteria in the *Clostridium* genus generate propionic acid, which can reduce your body's production of mood-boosting dopamine and serotonin. Microbes like Bifidobacterium enhance production of butyrate, an anti-inflammatory substance that keeps gut toxins out of the brain. Other species produce the amino acid tryptophan, a precursor to mood-balancing serotonin."[424]

As researchers continue to study the communication link between digestive system and the central nervous system, "many already think it creates a major potential avenue for mental-health treatment."[425] Microbes impact the mechanisms that can trigger mental illnesses like depression. "Even as scientists highlight these kinds of connections between gut microbe treatments and symptom improvement, the question of causality has lingered: Do gut bacterial changes actually drive mood and behavioral changes? A growing body of research suggests they do. ... One Australian study published in 2017 even suggests that a diet higher in beneficial bacteria can banish depression in more than a third of people."[426]

Research into gut microbes has uncovered that "people with more butyrate-producing gut microbes—such as certain types of *Faecalibacterium* and *Coprococcus*—have a higher quality of life, while people with lower levels of *Coprococcus* are more likely to be depressed."[427] One researcher predicted that soon a new type of therapy called "psychobiotics" will treat people with mental-health issues like depression by examining their gut microbiomes for imbalances before prescribing a tailored probiotic or fecal transplant as a corrective measure.[428]

More research needs to be done to flesh out those early discoveries, but for now, depression patients can try over-the-counter probiotics or probiotics in food, with caution. "While doctors generally regard common strains like *B. breve* and *L. acidophilus* as safe for human consumption—

they appear in foods like yogurt, kombucha and kefir—bacteria are bioactive substances, so ingesting them involves some level of risk. And in the U.S., the supplement industry is largely unregulated. That means consumers have to take companies' word that probiotics contain the strains listed on the label."[429]

If you want to explore the gut-brain connection, you can try fermented foods, including kefir, kimchi, kombucha, miso, and yogurt to give your gut bacteria diversity; avoid processed foods and food additives as much as possible, especially artificial sweeteners which can alter metabolism; lower your overall stress level; and consume more plants.[430]

**Holistic Medicine**
Holistic treatments for depression have a long history and some foresee a growing role for natural remedies. "So-called natural remedies for depression aren't a replacement for medical diagnosis and treatment. However, for some people certain herbal and dietary supplements do seem to work well, ... but more studies are needed to determine which are most likely to help and what side effects they might cause."[431]

According to Suzanne Norman, a holistic health practitioner in Libertyville, Illinois, "Typically, mental-health conditions are looked at as separate from the rest of the body. The holistic approach protocol employs diet and stress management along with mind and body practices to address the depressive symptoms."[432] Sometimes, holistic medicines are used along with those practices. Three holistic medicines that have gotten a lot of attention as potential depression treatments of the future are St. John's wort, SAMe (S-adenosylmethionine), and omega-3 fatty acids. All of them "show promise" for relieving depression.[433]

St. John's wort is an herbal supplement that has yet to receive the FDA's stamp of approval in the United States, but in Europe, it's been a popular treatment for depression.[434] Some recent research shows why "St. John's wort is actually one of the most effective herbal remedies to try for depression."[435] Research studies number in the dozens on the way this herb helps those with depression. "Overall, we found that the St. John's wort extracts tested in the trials were superior to placebos and as effective as standard antidepressants, with fewer side effects.' In other words, it works."[436]

SAMe, a supplement that's a synthetic form of a chemical occurring naturally in the human body, isn't yet approved by the FDA as an official depression treatment in the United States, but is widely prescribed by doctors to treat depression in Europe—just like St. John's wort.[437] The Mayo Clinic cautions that SAMe needs more studies to prove its efficacy but the chemical appears to be effective in the short term.[438]

Omega-3 fatty acids are healthy fats that are found in foods like fish and nuts. Nutritional supplements of omega-3 fatty acids are becoming popular as depression treatments. "Omega-3 fatty acids such as eicosapentaeoic acid (EPA) and docosahexaenoic acid (DHA) might have an impact on depression because these compounds are widespread in the brain. ... The evidence is not fully conclusive, but omega-3 supplements are an option. One to two grams of omega-3 fatty acids daily is the generally accepted dose for healthy individuals, but for patients with mental disorders, up to three grams has been shown to be safe and effective."[439] The Mayo Clinic noted that "although eating foods with omega-3 fatty acids appears to have heart-healthy benefits, more research is needed to determine if it has an effect on preventing or improving depression."[440]

Although these holistic medicines seem promising as depression treatments of the future, patients should check with their doctors and do their homework before taking these medicines. Nutritional supplements such as St. John's wort, SAMe, and omega-3 fatty acids are not currently regulated by the FDA in the United States, so "you can't always be certain of what you're getting and whether it's safe. It's best to do some research before starting any dietary supplement."[441]

It's also important for patients to consult their doctors before starting any supplements to prevent dangerous drug interactions with medications they are currently taking. Both St. John's wort and SAMe have been shown to interfere with some prescription antidepressant medications, so depression patients shouldn't take them together.[442]

Holistic medicine also encompasses non-supplemental treatments. Norman points out that she works with patients diagnosed with depression on "balancing their stressors in life. A big part of my job is getting people reconnected with their bodies because every choice they make can impact that balance." For example, she specifically addresses chronic pain, emotional imbalances or periods of emotional pain, physical well-being, body nourishment, and stress levels.

Holistic protocols now being rediscovered by medical professionals like Norman have been used for thousands of years. "To bring them into our contemporary medicine models demystifies these holistic ways that allows more people to receive the benefits from this approach," she says. More scientific studies are looking into how effective holistic medicine is in treating a variety of diseases, including depression. "It's a slow process in some parts of the United States, but more studies are coming out in support of holistic medicine, and the public perception that this is a viable alternative to treatment for diseases like depression is growing," adds Norman.

Each day, we learn more about depression and how it affects the patient, along with innovative ways to treat the symptoms and the disease itself. These discoveries bring hope to those suffering from depression for whom traditional treatments aren't working.

PART III: THE TREATMENT

# CHAPTER SIXTEEN
## ELECTROCONVULSIVE THERAPY TREATMENT AND DEPRESSION

**"Mark's electroconvulsive therapy treatments were the best thing in the world for him. While he didn't show improvement immediately, as he continued the course of the treatments, he gradually moved out of the deep depression."**
—My sister Robin Litzsinger

Shock treatment, or ECT, has been a highly controversial form of treatment for depression ever since it was first developed in 1938. It involves sending an electrical current through a patient's brain that is powerful enough to cause a convulsion similar to an epileptic seizure. In the process, the brain's chemistry undergoes changes that relieve the patient's depression. Because of the success rate of shock treatment for people suffering from the most severe cases of depression, doctors continue to proscribe its use today. "The modern version of ECT, far from outmoded, is the most effective therapy available for severe, treatment-resistant depression and bipolar disorder (and even sometimes, when deployed early enough, schizophrenia)."[443]

In part, the controversy and fear surrounding ECT has been fueled by its depiction on the silver screen in movies such as "The Snake Pit" (1948), "One Flew Over the Cuckoo's Nest" (1975), "Frances" (1982), and "Shine" (1996). Some patients who underwent shock treatment in these movies—and in real-life examples of early ECT—experienced significant side effects such as confusion, memory loss, heart problems, and broken bones. "There is no treatment in psychiatry more frightening than electroconvulsive therapy. ... There is also no treatment in psychiatry more effective than ECT."[444]

During the early years of its history, shock treatment was administered with little regard to the patient's well-being. For example, ECT was often given to patients without anesthesia; patients today are anesthetized to prevent them from injuring themselves during muscle spasms caused by seizures. In the past, doctors or medical staff sometimes didn't carefully monitor shock treatments to ensure electrical dosages were precise and didn't check patients' vital signs frequently during the procedure.

Those oversights decades ago meant ECT posed a greater risk to patients than it does today. However, the memory of these risks and side effects contributes to the controversy surrounding shock therapy as a depression treatment today, which can provide better results from more targeted procedures. "A procedure pioneered in the 1930s that seemed on the verge of extinction just a generation ago is being performed today at medical centers large and small. ... Madness no more, electric shock is quietly being resurrected as a restorative wonder that someday could rank right up there with penicillin and Prozac. ... How one of the most reviled psychiatric procedures is fast becoming one of its mainstays is ... a narrative that begins with an epidemic of mental illness that has stubbornly resisted a cure, and a handful of doctors who have equally stubbornly refused to give up on a remedy that most had banished as barbaric."[445]

### A Viable Option for Severe Cases of Depression
Patients usually pursue ECT only when they suffer from severe depression and haven't found enough relief from other forms of treatment. In particular, two types of patients tend to use shock therapy to treat their depression: suicidal patients and pregnant women who want to avoid the risks sometimes associated with antidepressants. "People who are afraid of taking their lives may request convulsant therapy as the only treatment that can stop their depression and suicidality right away. Also, pregnant

women who are so severely depressed that they are endangering their own lives and the lives of their babies can request convulsant therapy to put a rapid end to their depression. Most authorities agree that convulsant therapy is safer than medications for the baby because the convulsive stimulation bypasses the unborn child."[446]

Nowadays, ECT is used to treat severe depression for patients suffering from psychosis (detachment from reality), suicidal thoughts, not eating, and depression that doesn't respond to other treatments. "ECT may be a good treatment option when medications aren't tolerated or other forms of therapy haven't worked. In some cases, ECT is used during pregnancy, when medications can't be taken because they might harm the developing fetus, in older adults who can't tolerate drug side effects, in people who prefer ECT treatments over taking medications, [and] when ECT has been successful in the past."[447]

### The Early Years of Shock Therapy

ECT emerged as a treatment for depression in 1938 and went on to become widely used to treat severe cases of depression in the mid-twentieth century—despite the fact that it was associated with serious risks at that time. "Long ago, doctors witnessed immediate and dramatic depression recoveries after their patients had seizures, and they conceived of the seizure as a treatment [for depression]."[448] That discovery led to the development of shock therapy.

"Historically, there has been a long association of seizures and general improvement in psychiatric patients," says Dr. William Scheftner, psychopharmacologist and former chairman of the Department of Psychiatry at Rush University Medical Center in Chicago, Illinois. "For example, patients who have partial complex seizures often become irritable and unsociable prior to a seizure. After they have a seizure, they return to their usual personalities."

Early attempts to jolt patients into having seizures involved injecting them with chemicals. "The problem was that the chemicals used also had bad side effects, including necrosis [death of living cells or tissues] of the muscle," explains Dr. Scheftner. "Also, you never knew how long after the injection a patient would have a seizure. It could be five minutes or ten hours, which made chemical induction an iffy proposition."

The use of ECT as a more regular treatment for depression didn't catch on until after World War II. "It was at that point that this form of shock treatment for depression for various otherwise untreatable conditions came about, and from there, it became increasingly more popular."[449]

By 1945, American psychiatric hospitals were widely using electroshock procedures. At the time, many psychiatrists recognized the potential benefits of the treatment in some patients, noting that when ECT worked, it had an immediate effect on the patient with few side effects. However, administering ECT had its dangers, including too strong convulsions, which could result in broken bones, broken teeth, or a bitten tongue. "A few patients complained of some memory loss, though this usually appeared to be short-term. Many patients, particularly those who had suffered severe, prolonged, and crippling depression, improved dramatically."[450]

### Improvements Lead to Wider Acceptance

Despite a rocky beginning, ECT came back into favor during the latter part of the twentieth century and the first part of the twenty-first century following a variety of improvements that reduced its risks. However, the fact that ECT was given to some patients in the 1950s and '60s without their informed consent contributed to the treatment's controversial reputation.

In the 1950s and '60s, doctors could order the procedure for their hospitalized patients without their consent, and families could likewise request the treatment when committing relatives to mental institutions. This practice was prohibited by the 1974 National Research Act, which established the medical policy of "informed consent." According to Alex Groberman in his article, "Shock Treatments for Depression," "one of the most well-known standards of modern ECT is 'informed consent.' As per the [U.S.] Surgeon General, the only time involuntary shock treatments for depression is permitted is in the extreme cases when all other options have been exhausted. Or, of course, if it is deemed that the ECT can be potentially life-saving."[451]

The medical community worked to try to decrease the risks associated with shock therapy during the latter years of the twentieth century, when doctors began to perform the procedure with anesthesia and under carefully monitored conditions. This substantially reduced the risks of the most worrisome side effects from earlier years, such as memory loss and physical injuries from the seizures. "ECT is much safer today and is given to people while they're under general anesthesia. … Although ECT still causes some side effects, it now uses electrical currents given in a controlled setting to achieve the most benefit with the fewest possible risks."[452]

During the 1990s, ECT began to be used with a much lower voltage to avoid memory loss or memory distortion. As author Jonathan Engel found in researching his book, *American Therapy*, "patients who submitted to a full regimen of ten to fifteen treatments recovered rapidly from severe depression. … One patient described his experience[:] 'It is a nonentity, a nothing. You go to sleep, and when you wake up, it is all over. It is easier to take than going to the dentist.'"[453]

### When ECT Is an Effective Treatment

What makes patients agree to ECT? The effectiveness of the treatment in giving depressed people immediate relief from their symptoms. "Bilateral ECT [which places the electrodes on both temples] works in roughly 70 to 80 percent of all depressions," notes out Dr. Scheftner. "Unilateral ECT [which places one electrode on the crown of the head, the other on either the right or left temple] appears to be somewhat less effective, given the current devices we have."

A study by the Consortium for Research in ECT found an 87 percent remission rate among severely depressed patients who received shock therapy. The study also found that ECT decreased the chance of relapse as effectively as the use of antidepressant medications when the patients followed up with additional ECT treatments.[454] The consortium notes that shock therapy "often works when other treatments are unsuccessful. … ECT can provide rapid, significant improvements in severe symptoms of a number of mental health conditions." [455]

Today, ECT is considered a generally safe procedure with minimal risks of side effects, such as confusion, memory loss, nausea, headaches, jaw and/or muscle pain, heart rate and/or blood pressure changes, and complications from receiving anesthesia. "The mortality from the procedure itself is from general anesthetic," says Dr. Scheftner. "Particularly for elderly patients there appears to be some evidence that those with significant depression—enough to bring them to a hospital— who have ECT enjoy a longer lifespan than those with a similar severe depression."

### Changing the Brain's Chemistry

Medical professionals have yet to pinpoint exactly how shock therapy relieves depression, but they do know that ECT changes the brain's chemistry in a way that quickly reverses the symptoms of depression. "No one knows for certain how ECT helps treat severe depression and other mental illnesses. What is known, though, is that many chemical aspects of brain function are changed during and after seizure activity. These chemical changes may build upon one another, somehow reducing symptoms of severe depression or other mental illnesses. That's why ECT is most effective in people who receive a full course of multiple treatments." [456]

Depressed people can undergo shock therapy either in a hospital or on an outpatient basis. During each procedure, an electrical current goes from electrodes placed on patients' skulls to their brains, causing a seizure that lasts under a minute. The anesthetic and muscle relaxant keeps the patient calm and unaware of the seizure. [457] "In the United States, ECT treatments are generally given two to three times weekly for three to four weeks—for a total of six to twelve treatments. The number of treatments you'll need depends on the severity of your symptoms and how rapidly they improve." [458]

"We'd gone through everything with Mark, and he'd get a mediocre response or a modest response," says Dr. Scheftner. "We were in a position with his depression that we had to go to something which continues to be the most certain of all treatments for major depression: electric convulsive therapy."

When Dr. Scheftner first broached the subject of ECT as a treatment option, I was a bit nervous, but I was in a bad state of depression, and the traditional methods of treating it with medication weren't working. This was the worse depression I'd ever had. Treatments that had worked before didn't now, and even the new medications had no effect. That's when shock therapy came up.

Most people when they hear about ECT are nervous because of how it has been portrayed in the movies. For me, I frankly didn't have much of a choice if I wanted to recover from this depression. I agreed to try it, especially because my sisters and my father were very supportive. My sisters took me to the treatments. I received the ECT treatments as an outpatient under a twilight sedative. I had a succession of them about once a week, plus talk therapy to help with my ruminations.

Testimonies abound of patients who experience remission or relief from depression after ECT—even though no one quite knows how this happens. Researchers and doctors have provided a multitude of theories over the years. "The seizure could be key, or shutting off the process that produces seizures. It could center around the electricity, or the same biochemical reactions that make antidepressants work. Many patients prefer to think of ECT as somehow resetting the brain when it gets out of balance, the same way rebooting a balky [uncooperative] computer sometimes fixes it."[459]

Other theories about how ECT works include the idea that inducing an epileptic seizure "can stop even the most severe depression suddenly and completely, likely because seizures naturally release an immediate flood of serotonin, norepinephrine, and dopamine into the brain. Seizures also release brain-healing BDNF [brain-derived neurotrophic factor], which repairs stress-damaged brain cells and causes new brain cells to be born and proliferate in areas of the brain that have been damaged by unipolar major depression."[460]

Although shock therapy usually leads to some immediate relief of depression symptoms, it doesn't cure depression, so follow-up treatments of some kind are necessary. Most patients who experience ECT notice an improvement after a few treatments. "Full improvement may take longer. Response to antidepressant medications, in comparison, can take several weeks or more. Even after your symptoms improve, you'll still need ongoing treatment to prevent a recurrence. ... Known as maintenance therapy, that ongoing treatment doesn't have to be ECT, but it can be. More often, it includes antidepressants or other medications, or psychological counseling (psychotherapy)."[461]

### The Evolution of ECT

Because shock therapy is still proving to be an effective treatment for severe depression, and methods for the procedure continue to evolve, it will likely remain a solid treatment choice for depressed people in the years to come. "It is counterintuitive to see a treatment as time-consuming and tangled as ECT catch on in this era of Prozac and the quick fix. ... Most surprising of all, ECT is the only remedy in mainstream medicine that is expanding in use, receiving increased attention in research, and offering life-saving hope to tens of thousands of people, even as much as the public believes it is extinct."[462]

Looking toward the future, some unanswered questions about shock therapy still remain. Researchers are still searching for answers as to why ECT relieves the symptoms of depression. "Questions also remain about the price shock patients pay in memories lost, in rare cases permanently, and whether such risks can be minimized or eliminated entirely. The rise, fall, and rise again of ECT remains an epic without an ending, as practitioners and potential patients alike wait to see if hopes for success are sustained."[463]

According to Dr. Scheftner, "while memory problems can occur with ECT, there are very few medical problems that prevent the use of ECT. I think most people would choose a further interesting life after ECT than continue to suffer from depression."

Whatever happened, ECT worked for me because it cleared the cobwebs from my mind. Within a year of starting ECT treatments, I was operating on a different, better level. Not only was I well, but I also was thinking more clearly and was interested in many more things. My mind was questioning, I could synthesize information very quickly, and come to deductions about personal and business decisions like never before.

After the treatments, I broadened my learning and interests to encompass new areas in life, including politics, world affairs, travel, culture, and entrepreneurship. I was on the family company's board, and began giving back philanthropically and living by the Golden Rule by being a good person and helping people wherever I could. I realized that many of us are so busy in our lives (self-centered and self-absorbed) that we miss easy opportunities to help people on a daily basis. It's not just about money; it's about helping someone when they need it. So I started looking for ways to help others, such as assisting an older person to put their walker in the trunk of his or her car, opening a door for someone at a restaurant, or helping someone jumpstart a car on a cold winter's day. Simple stuff that's easy for all of us to think about and do.

This lingering stigma about shock treatments may keep some depressed people from talking about the option with their doctors. As more people like me talk about their success with ECT, my hope is that more depressed people will be able to experience the hope of a renewed life after undergoing electroconvulsive therapy.

PART III: THE TREATMENT

# CHAPTER SEVENTEEN
## TALK THERAPY AND DEPRESSION

"Negative thinking patterns can be immensely deceptive and persuasive, and change is rarely easy. But with patience and persistence, I believe that nearly all individuals suffering from depression can improve and experience a sense of joy and self-esteem once again."
—David D. Burns, Stanford University professor and author of *Feeling Good: The New Mood Therapy*

O ver the years, doctors and others have found that therapy—talk, animal/dog, and exercise—can be extremely beneficial to people with depression, especially when accompanied by medication and other treatments. One of the most popular forms of therapy for depression is talk therapy (also called counseling), in which depressed people talk about their thoughts and feelings with others (such as psychiatrists, clinical social workers, psychologists, and support-group members) with the goal of managing or recovering from the disease. Every form of talk therapy focuses in some way on helping depressed people understand how they can tap into the power of their minds to heal.

What's vital about talk therapy is that it helps a patient to recognize patterns of thinking that might hinder the person's recovery. When a patient becomes aware of those patterns, he or she can choose how to respond to the thoughts or "diminish the power thoughts have over your mood and life. This transformation allows you to evaluate behaviors objectively. We become aware of the mental processes that are driving our behavior. Then we have the opportunity to look objectively at those thoughts or feelings, and decide whether we want to respond in our habitual way or try something new."[464]

"Sometimes through talk therapy alone, people with mild to moderate depression improve," notes Bonnie Senner,[465] an integrative psychodynamic therapist in the Chicago area. "Talk therapy works for these people when the depression stems from the current situation or when the past colors how they view the world and relate to others. Patients gain insight into how the past is impacting the present, leaving them in a stronger place when the depression lifts. Depressions that have a biological origin frequently need medication in addition to talk therapy. I recommend early in treatment that people get a psychiatric evaluation to see if medication is indicated, or if the medication their internist prescribed is the best one. I often refer them to a psychopharmacologist, who has an expertise in medication management."

Although there's a plethora of different types of talk therapy available from counselors, the two types that have proven to be the most effective (and are also most commonly used) are cognitive therapy (which also is called cognitive behavioral therapy, or CBT) and interpersonal therapy. "CBT focuses on looking at how negative thought patterns may be affecting your mood. The therapist helps you learn how to make positive changes in your thoughts and behaviors. Interpersonal therapy focuses on how you relate to others and helps you make positive changes in your personal relationships. Both types of therapy can be effective in treating depression."[466]

Choosing which type of therapy to pursue—for example, cognitive, interpersonal, psychodynamic therapy (focuses on the past), or family therapy (focuses on relationships)—involves figuring out what your personal goals are for recovery, then discussing the specifics of your depression experience with a therapist with whom you may potentially develop a counseling relationship. During the first session, the therapist will ask detailed questions about those goals, including why you are seeking help and what you hope to accomplish through therapy. "For example, are you looking for ways to better deal with personal relationships, or are you hoping to set goals for yourself and make changes? It's helpful to be as honest as you can with your therapist about your depression and your goals for therapy. After listening to your situation, the therapist should be able to tell you what type of treatment he [or she] recommends and come up with a treatment plan for you."[467]

Remember that more than one approach might be helpful in your recovery. "Talk therapy along with medication can help with depression," says Senner. "Patients feel heard and understood because you develop a relationship with them. It can pull them out of the depression as they feel heard and understood, especially in a time when the rest of the world isn't understanding them."

## Cognitive Therapy

Using cognitive therapy, people who are suffering from depression can learn how to transform negative thoughts into positive ones that promote healing. The most common approach is with CBT, which many therapists use when treating depressed patients.[468]

Cognitive therapists act like coaches when working with patients. The behavioral component centers on the exact steps the patient can do, such as utilizing a relaxation technique or adding fun activities to their calendar. The cognitive aspect examines the patient's usual thought patterns and delves into how those patterns could elongate or stifle the episode. Then solutions to overcoming those patterns are discussed. "The therapist is like a coach, helping you master both the cognitive and behavioral skills. Just as if you were learning to play soccer or the violin, great emphasis is placed on *practice*."[469]

The process of changing ingrained thought patterns requires sustained effort from patients. There are many different cognitive-therapy techniques to assist in that transformation. "Perhaps the most important is the questioning and testing of thoughts, assumptions, and beliefs to determine whether they are realistic. The aim is to identify inaccurate thoughts that may result in depression and subsequently counter these thinking patterns with objective evidence."[470]

Cognitive therapy has been widely tested in research studies—perhaps more so than any other type of talk therapy—and has been proven to be effective. I had actually gone to see a talk therapist for another reason when I became engulfed with depression. My therapist then took on the role of support with talk therapy during my depression. I think she probably took the burden off my siblings and my father because I was talking more to her than to them during the episode. And since she was a professional, she knew how to deal with depression and was better able to help me get through it.

"Like many talk therapists, I help patients gain insights into how their past is impacting their present, which leaves them in a stronger place when the depression lifts," explains Senner. "That is why talk therapy can be so beneficial to depressed patients."

### Cognitive Therapy and Antidepressants

Studies, including several rather large ones, have found cognitive therapy "to be as effective as antidepressant medications for the treatment of mild to moderate depression."[471] One of those studies was conducted by Robert J. DeRubeis, Greg J. Siegle, and Steven D. Hollon, who wrote that "cognitive therapy is as efficacious as antidepressant medications at treating depression, and it seems to reduce the risk of relapse even after its discontinuation. Cognitive therapy and antidepressant medication probably engage some similar neural mechanisms, as well as mechanisms that are distinctive to each."[472]

Medication is often thought of as the first approach to try for depression treatment, but CBT may have a more lasting impact. "Studies that look at the combination of medication and CBT suggest that people get a faster start, feeling better after twelve weeks or so on medication plus CBT, but that in the long run, many people do well utilizing CBT methods without any medication. There is growing evidence that building positive brain circuitry will balance and offset the brain circuits for ruminative, negative thinking, so techniques that enhance feeling centered, spirituality, and positive emotion will be of great value."[473]

The effectiveness of cognitive therapy for treating depression has been found to prevent relapse after treatment has ended. However, patients utilizing medication alone often need to continue that medicine to prevent a relapse.[474] Cognitive therapy (CT) may be the best overall talk-therapy choice for most people with depression. Overall, "CT is a powerful method that can help us change our thinking patterns and feel better emotionally."[475]

"Cognitive behavioral therapy is popular today because it is amenable to research and can be done in a short time period," notes Senner. "But it does not work for everyone. With a new patient who is depressed, I do a thorough evaluation and recommend a psychiatric evaluation as well. A 2010 study[476] showed that psychodynamic therapy was as effective as other evidence-based therapies, but also that the benefits of psychodynamic therapy appeared to be longer lasting."

## Interpersonal Therapy

Depressed people who would like to figure out how to fight depression by improving the quality of their relationships may prefer interpersonal therapy (IPT) instead of cognitive therapy. "IPT is a well-known treatment that has been shown to be as effective as antidepressants in mild to moderate depression. It focuses on a person's relationships and tries to improve the quality of the most important ones."[477]

Just like cognitive therapy, interpersonal therapy has been shown to be effective by many different research studies. IPT zeroes in on problems with interpersonal relationships that could contribute to depression, and also examines problems that depression may cause or exacerbate in relating to others. "Multiple studies have confirmed the effectiveness of IPT for the acute and maintenance treatment of depression. IPT is a time-limited, here-and-now therapy that focuses on developing an understanding of the interpersonal problems in one's life and then developing concrete solutions."[478]

## Talking With Loved Ones

Another way people suffering from depression can pursue talk therapy is simply by talking with caring, trustworthy friends or family about what they're going through. By engaging in conversations about their illness with those in their personal support group, depressed people can express their thoughts and feelings freely, and hopefully gain some valuable insights that they can use in the healing process.

In my early depressions, I would call my father and siblings to talk. It was extremely helpful to me, but I think sometimes it ended up being overwhelming for them to listen to my ruminations and repetitions.

"Mark would call us all the time," says my sister Shawn, noting that being a partner in talk therapy can be a challenge. "Depression is a selfish disease because you can become self-absorbed. It doesn't cross your mind because you're only focused on the fact that you're frightened of something or you've got to work something out. That selfish side is very hard on the family. But at the same time, you [the family member or friend] feel guilty because you don't have it and you wouldn't wish it on anybody. So you do the right thing. And I know it wasn't just me that he called; he called all of my siblings. He may have had us on a rotation. He could have called me at one a.m., another sibling at two a.m., etc. I do know he talked to all of us during his depression episodes."

Turning to friends or family for help tends to be less effective than talking with professional therapists because your personal support group typically hasn't been specially trained to treat depression. But talk therapy with loved ones can complement professional talk therapy, and for depressed people who, for whatever reason, don't want to pursue professional therapy, talking with friends and family about their depression is better than not talking about it at all.

The support from close friends, family, and the community helps those with depression stay connected to the world. "Social connection helps push the brain in an antidepressant direction, turning down activity in stress circuitry, and boosting the activity of feel-good brain chemicals like dopamine and serotonin. That's why it makes sense to swim hard against the tide of our 'culture of isolation' and to place our relationships at the very top of the priority list. Truly, nothing in life matters more."[479]

Talking with a personal support group provides a valuable sense of community that can have healing benefits by pulling depressed people out of isolation. Depressed people can "find authentic community, and the profound sense of belonging it confers"[480] from places of worship, volunteer organizations, social clubs, self-help groups, special-interest or hobby groups, sports leagues, and their workplaces.

Although loved ones will likely give depressed people lots of encouragement, that isn't the most effective tactic to help fight the illness. It is more impactful to distract a person from the struggle with depression and toward fun social activities. Reassuring a depressed person rarely triggers a better outlook in the patient. In fact, positive words can clash "so sharply with the depressed individual's negative self-view that [they are] dismissed almost immediately. Ironically, the best way to combat depressive feelings of insecurity is often to ignore [expressions of insecurity], to divert attention instead to more engaging social activities that have the power to lift mood and shift the brain into a less negative mode of thinking."[481]

For those who might not have a circle of friends or family to turn to, some countries are exploring peer-support groups or training elders to aid people suffering from depression. In Zimbabwe, for example, 300 elders have been trained to sit on a park bench outside a clinic and talk through problems with patients. "On any given afternoon in the capital of Harare and nearby cities, an elder woman can be found on a bench outside a clinic, listening intently to another person's stories."[482] With research supporting the efficacy of "social-support methods of care"[483] in treating mental illnesses, having someone trained and waiting to listen can provide the safety net people need.

### Active Participation

Depressed people who actively participate in talk therapy get the maximum benefits. William Marchand, in his book, *Depression and Bipolar Disorder: Your Guide to Recovery,* puts it this way: "I like the analogy of working with a coach to develop athletic ability. No matter how good the coach is, no improvement in skills will occur without lots of practice. Sitting in a therapist's office once a week is likely to have limited benefit unless it is accompanied by effort on a daily basis to implement changes."[484]

Patients who listen to encouragement from their therapists to stay motivated can experience good outcomes from talk therapy. "Initially, [the patient's] treatment will focus on finding motivation that you can hang onto, and it will progress no faster than [the patient's] mental energy can allow. The close observation and continuing assessment of the therapist can promote that motivation."[485]

## Have Patience

Talk therapy isn't a "quick fix" for depressed patients. "Depression, especially major depression, can take a very long time to lift," points out Senner.

Talk therapy involves the gradual process of talking about your thoughts and feelings, and figuring out the best ways to change negative patterns to overcome depression. You may need to change therapists a few times until you find one whose approach is a good match for you. So try to have patience.

It will take time to discover what works best for you and to heal. For example, what really benefited me was just sitting down with my therapist and talking about how things were going, especially if I had a bad day. It helped that we were able to talk about more than just my depression.

Over time, those with depression will start to notice improvement in moods or relationships with others. "If you aren't feeling any better, talk with your therapist. [He or] she may be able to try another approach to therapy or refer you for other kinds of treatment. Or you might benefit from seeing someone else. You may need to see more than one therapist to find the type of therapy that's right for you. Therapy is not always easy and can sometimes even be painful as you work through difficult problems. But if you stick with it, talk therapy can also be gratifying and rewarding—and can give you the tools you need to help ease your depression."[486]

PART III: THE TREATMENT

# CHAPTER EIGHTEEN
## ANIMAL THERAPY AND DEPRESSION

**"In a way, we could all use a psychiatric service or therapy dog because of the incredible amount of stress that we're all under."**
—Dr. Carole Lieberman, American psychiatrist

Healing from depression may come in the form of a dog's wagging tail and sloppy kiss, a cat's soft snuggle and loud purr, or a bird's playful antics and cheerful song. Animals, whose companionship has comforted humans throughout history, can play important roles in the healing process for depressed people.

"The earliest reported use of pets as therapy[487] occurred in eighteenth-century England," says Callandre Cozzolino,[488] executive director of Canine Therapy Corps (CT Corps) in Chicago, Illinois. "The first documented usage in the United States was in New York during World War II."

Dogs and other pets might not have been formally used as therapy until recently in this country, but domesticated animals have long been living with humans, bringing them solace and companionship.

### A Dog's Life

Dogs have been domesticated animals and living as part of the community with humans for thousands of years.[489] The bond between humans and dogs can be unbreakable. "The ability and intuition of dogs coupled with their enthusiasm and lust for life really make them suitable for making us feel better, which is the purpose of animal therapy," notes Cozzolino.

Canines provide comfort and friendship to all who own them, but it's only been rather recently that dogs have been trained to assist in a depressed person's therapy and rehabilitation. "Service and assistance dogs have been helping owners have more freedom to accomplish more on their own for years," says Cozzolino. "But only lately have we realized how the amazing companionship dogs offer can be translated into helping people with depression and other mental illnesses get better."

The rise of canines as service animals became formalized after World War I.[490] However, in the early days of dogs being used for therapy, there was a reluctance to have the animals in public-health settings, like a hospital. "It was quite the paradigm shift of risk versus reward to get doctors and others in the medical field to accept the small risk of having animals in a hospital setting," says Cozzolino. "The positive, therapeutic value of having animals there to help the patients in their recovery outweighs any of the risks, which are low."

CT Corps works with institutions like hospitals to establish dog-therapy programs. "We help those places establish protocols for the dogs, such as using only one entrance/exit, putting a sheet down if the dog will be on a chair or bed, having plenty of hand sanitizer available, etc. These make the visits less risky and improve the time spent with the patients," explains Cozzolino.

The very act of caring for animals can be therapeutic in and of itself. "Pets have an almost magical ability to increase our sense of well-being through their affectionate physical contact, which lowers stress hormones and boosts the activity of feel-good brain chemicals like dopamine and serotonin. Pets also provide us with a faithful source of social companionship, and a deep feeling that we truly *matter*: They literally depend on us for their very lives."[491]

Research into the benefits of animal therapy continues, but studies so far suggest that depressed people can gain myriad healing benefits from spending time with animals. "Benefits may include enhanced socialization; reduced levels of stress, anxiety, and loneliness; improved mood; and development of recreation skills. ... There is some preliminary evidence that having an animal friend may support your recovery."[492]

Studies have found that animals lower tension and improve a person's overall mood, but the primary benefit may be unconditional love. That unconditional love can give those with depression hope and comfort.

Cozzolino has found that a patient's mood can improve from just one visit with a dog. "Petting a dog can lower a person's resting heart rate and for those in a recovery room after an operation, a therapy dog reduces the need for pain medication," she says. "That simple touch has many benefits."

In addition, the available evidence suggests that depressed people who have dogs involved in their therapy work longer and harder at their own recovery. "It gives them a distraction from their own thoughts," says Cozzolino. "A dog makes repetitive tasks seem less repetitive and more fun, such as tossing a ball by yourself versus tossing a ball to a dog."

Benefits of animal therapy include:
- **Simple love.** If your relationships with family and friends are difficult and unraveled, a pet can provide the antidote to feelings of frustration and of being unloved. Pets won't get frustrated with you or give unwanted advice; they love you for who you are.
- **Responsibility.** The idea of taking care of another living thing may seem too hard for a person with depression, especially when taking care of oneself is challenging. But experts point out that increasing a person's responsibility, such as with a pet, can give new focus to the life of a depressed person.
- **Activity.** Depression can make it hard for someone to get exercise—something that helps boost mood. Pets can provide the impetus to get moving. Dogs need to be walked, and even cats, fish, and birds have needs that can give a person a reason to get up and about.
- **Routine.** Pets offer those with depression a built-in daily schedule, which can be lifesaving. Most domestic animals have natural

habits—such as waking the owner up in the morning and being persistent in demanding walks and food—that provide a person with daily structure.

- **Companionship.** By its very nature, depression tends to isolate those who suffer from it. Depressed people often pull back from family and friends, but a pet means the person has constant companionship.
- **Social interaction.** Pets can gently nudge their owners into more social contact, such as chatting with fellow dog walkers while at the park or visiting with other pet owners while waiting at the vet. Pets offer a natural icebreaker with other people.
- **Touch.** Studies have found that we feel better when we have physical contact with others, and pets offer the opportunity to regularly touch another living being. Petting cats or dogs can sooth frazzled emotions and lower heart rates.
- **Better health.** Research has shown that dog ownership lowers stress hormones and blood pressure, while increasing feel-good chemicals in the brain.

What kind of pet should you choose to help heal your depression? Dogs are by nature social animals and may be an especially good choice for depressed people interested in pursuing animal therapy. Dogs deliver unconditional love in an enthusiastic manner. "They don't care if we have a bad hair day or aren't in the best mood; our canine companions will always be there for us. Of course, other animals can also be great companions, but I think the love that dogs have for humans is a great example of what we can get from our furry friends."[493]

Cats are popular animal-therapy choices too, because they like to snuggle and play with their human companions, and a cat's purr is soothing. But if adopting a dog or cat isn't practical—for example, if you're allergic or concerned about the cost and time needed for their care—other animals also can be helpful companions and ease depression symptoms. "Birds can be surprisingly affectionate. ... While you may not want to snuggle with a fish or a turtle, caring for them could also improve your mood. It creates responsibility and a new focus. Studies have shown that watching fish can lower your pulse and ease muscle tension too."[494]

The demand for pets soared during the pandemic as people sought the comfort animals provide during a stressful and uncertain time. Dogs have been there to provide emotional support to first-responders and victims after tragic events like 9/11. Animals have become an integral part of our society and it is likely more doctors and health-care professionals will begin to see the benefits of incorporating dogs and other animals in the healing process. "Some therapists incorporate pet therapy into their counseling sessions, allowing patients to stroke or cuddle a dog while working through issues with the counselor," says CT Corps' Cozzolino. "That can help patients relax in therapy and open up, resulting in an increased willingness to share important information with their therapists."

Dogs for certified therapy don't require the task-based training of a service animal. "There is also another category of dogs separate and distinct [from] service animals and therapy animals called emotional-support animals. Emotional-support animals can simply be well-behaved pets, and they are allowed to live with their owners," explains Cozzolino.

She pictures a bright future for pet therapy with more hospitals allowing dogs on the floor to help patients in their recovery and more psychologists using dogs or recommending patients get dogs. "There is a lot more to be done in this area, but as more studies are done, I'm sure pet therapy will grow to become an accepted form of depression treatment," says Cozzolino.

### Dog Therapy in Action

Canine Therapy Corps works with groups of people with mental illness and substance abuse, as well as with military veterans. One effective program is a dog-handling class that lasts between six and ten weeks. "They're expected to be here every week, which can be challenging," says Callandre Cozzolino, executive director of the Chicago, Illinois-based organization.

The program teaches participants perseverance, patience, how to maintain a positive attitude, and how to break down a task into manageable pieces. One of the exercises that helps participants practice these skills involves navigating a small agility course with their therapy dogs. Participants prepare mentally by memorizing the course. Then they have to be able to stay positive and connected to their dog even if they make a mistake while going through the course. Plus, they also are encouraged to have fun working with the dogs.

"Many [participants] after a session will tell us how much better they feel," says Cozzolino. "It's given them a reprieve from their life and they leave feeling a little bit more rejuvenated."

PART III: THE TREATMENT

# CHAPTER NINETEEN
## EXERCISE AND DEPRESSION

**"Exercise is probably the single most-effective depression-defeater you can do."**
—Margaret Wehrenberg, American author of *The 10 Best-Ever Depression Management Techniques*

Exercise is one of the most beneficial treatments for depression. The two types of exercise that studies have shown are most effective in fighting depression—aerobic exercise and yoga—are fairly easy to incorporate into people's daily lives. But while many depression patients know that exercising is good for them, they often have trouble actually doing the exercise as depression saps people's energy and motivation.

Studies have shown that physical activity at a higher level can correspond with lower depression levels. "Further, a fairly large body of literature suggests that aerobic exercise may be associated with reduced depressive symptoms. There is also some evidence for the benefits of nonaerobic exercise. Reviews of the evidence published in scientific journals generally conclude that exercise is beneficial for depression."[495]

"Exercise is important for overall mental stability," says Zak Rivera,[496] a personal trainer with Focused Results in Lake Bluff, Illinois. "Exercise gives people a sense of purpose and direction. I've noticed that when someone comes in for a training session dragging a little bit that after the workout, the majority of the time, they are smiling—even though they are dripping with sweat and tired."

People with depression can quickly reap the rewards of exercise. "Exercise is extraordinarily important for maintaining both physical and mental health. Aerobic exercise is the most potent antidepressant activity ever discovered, with the ability to reverse the toxic effects of depression on the brain. Physical activity even has mood-elevating effects that can usually be felt in a matter of minutes."[497]

## A Brain Changer

Because exercise changes the activity of brain chemicals just like medication does, it can be as powerful in treating the disease as antidepressants, although medications should be used along with an exercise routine in most depression cases. "Medication isn't the only way to correct brain abnormalities in depression. Physical exercise also brings about profound changes in the brain—changes that rival those seen with the most potent antidepressant medications."[498]

Exercise literally changes the brain, similar to what happens when taking antidepressant medicines. Exercise bumps up the activity of dopamine and serotonin, important chemicals in our brain that can get pushed off track by depression. "It also stimulates the brain's release of a key growth hormone (BDNF), which in turn helps reverse the toxic, brain-damaging effects of depression. It even sharpens memory and concentration, and helps us think more clearly. Simply put, *exercise is medicine*—one that affects the brain more powerfully than any drug."[499]

"Exercise gets the endorphins going—those feel-good hormones moving inside your body," notes Rivera. "It also gives people a goal. When they make an appointment with me, it keeps them accountable. As the workouts progress, they see their body and stamina changing too."

Like SSRI medications (see Chapter 13 for more on these medicines), exercise increases the serotonin levels in the brain, albeit in different ways. "Exercise … may affect serotonin levels more positively in people who have problems with serotonin, as seen in research with depressed persons. … Exercise also enhances BDNF to encourage the production of new brain cells that can produce serotonin. Additionally, it increases blood flow to the brain, which is associated with many aspects of brain health, and it can affect your neurotransmitter levels as well as the overall functioning of parts of the brain."[500]

**Aerobic Exercise**

The best type of exercise to fight depression is aerobic exercise, which a variety of research studies have shown to be more effective at reducing depression symptoms than any other form of exercise. Researchers think that aerobic exercise works against depression by releasing endorphin hormones in the body that help grow back parts of the brain that have shrunk due to the disease. "Researchers have ... consistently observed a powerful therapeutic benefit from *aerobic* exercise—the kind of workout that causes your heart rate to stay elevated for several minutes at a time."[501] Common aerobic exercises are running or jogging, fast walking, swimming, biking, hiking, dancing, stair climbing, racquetball or tennis, and team sports.

Rivera utilizes boxing and kickboxing along with SlamBall™ (a form of basketball played with four trampolines in front of each net and boards around the court edge). "There's something about boxing or SlamBall that's empowering and that can help a person get out any negative energy," he says. "However, any exercise will get those positive feelings going."

The effects of aerobic exercise on depression are still being studied. However, it appears that the power of aerobic exercise to release endorphins is most likely what makes it such a successful treatment. "The endorphin hypothesis suggests that exercise releases endorphin neurotransmitters, which results in the decrease of depressive symptoms."[502]

Aerobic exercise also treats depression by reducing stress. "Exercise is a prime stress reliever. ... For the depressed person with a lot of agitation, physical activities are better sources of stress relief than sitting still. Aerobic exercise is best, because it is a great long-term relaxer."[503]

When depressed people are doing aerobic exercise they enjoy, their minds can move away from negative thoughts and toward positive thoughts that promote healing. "Time really does fly when we're caught up in something enjoyable, even when there's physical exercise involved."[504]

The simplest way to get aerobic exercise—walking—is easy to begin and a good choice for depressed people who are struggling with low energy and motivation. "Walking has the absolute best record for easy access. ... The director of the Bipolar Clinic associated with Harvard, Dr. Gary Sachs, says, 'Here's your exercise program: go to the door, look at your watch. Walk 7.5 minutes in any direction, then turn around and walk home. Do that five days a week at least.'"[505] Walking is the best antidepressant form of exercise because "our bodies are designed for it—and because it's something just about everyone can do."[506]

So how much aerobic exercise should depressed people try to do? No official standards have been set yet, but health experts recommend patients do 90 to 105 minutes of aerobic exercise a week to produce an antidepressant effect.[507]

"I like to see my clients at least two or three times a week because that ensures if they happen to miss one workout, they have another scheduled fairly soon," says Rivera, who recommends at least six hours of aerobic activity weekly—but that may be something a person with depression would need to build up to.

What's most important is simply getting started with any amount of aerobic exercise. Then, you can gradually set higher exercise goals. "Educate yourself on the importance of exercise. Find a type of exercise you enjoy. What opportunities do you have to do it? Decide the largest possible step you can reasonably take in the direction of exercise. Get a partner if possible. Commit to an action plan. Be accountable. Keep track of what you do. Evaluate your progress and increase your goal regularly until you hit your target for the prescription for exercise."[508]

## Yoga

Yoga is a lower-impact form of exercise that researchers have found effective in depression treatment. Yoga fights depression through the endorphin-releasing benefits of physical exercise as well as the positive-thinking benefits of mindfulness. "Although aerobic exercise is good ... yoga is another means of promoting mental health."[509]

Daily yoga practice has been said to bring a person's physical body and emotions back into balance. "You will feel more energy, love yourself more, and have a happier life."[510]

Yoga's distinctive message to people who feel broken by their depression is that they are still whole as human beings—and by focusing on their wholeness, their depression may be reduced. "Even beneath ... the agony of depression, yoga says, you are whole. ... When you step onto your yoga mat, you are reminded of that wholeness, and the practice clears a pathway through your symptoms to the ground of your being, that which is your natural state."[511] In addition, depression often produces a feeling that the person is separated from himself, wondering, "What is wrong with me?" Yoga approaches from the opposite perspective of "What is right with me?"[512]

Practicing yoga requires a person to concentrate on the poses, thus shifting their focus toward something positive. "The highs, lows, the extremes of all the emotions are brought into balance by the physical practice, and the mind is soothed by the philosophy."[513] Each yoga stage relieves the practitioner from obsessed and negative thoughts. "To learn the pose your mind must focus on the details of alignment. Later, when you're in the pose and you allow your mind to become absorbed in the sensations in your body, you are very far from your everyday troubles."[514]

To use yoga to treat depression, patients should practice regularly with a qualified teacher as well as self-practice daily as well. "Simple spinal flexes on your hands and knees, a twist, a mountain pose, remembering to breathe long and deep through your nostrils, may be a good beginning."[515]

Overall, any exercise can have a positive impact on depressed patients. Remember to consult with your regular doctor before starting any exercise.

## Putting Personal Trainers Into Play

Personal training came into vogue during the first half of the twentieth century in America, although various cultures—including Greek and Roman—did have fitness training for athletic events and warfare in ancient times. Jack LaLanne, a fitness and nutritional expert who opened what many deem the first health club in the United States in 1936,[516] is often credited with popularizing personal training.

In 1954, the American College of Sports Medicine in Indianapolis was founded with the goal of promoting health and fitness, and providing certification for fitness professionals, including personal trainers. But it took until the 1980s for personal training as a career to take off.

Here are some things to consider when thinking about working with a personal trainer to help alleviate depression symptoms. Remember to consult your physician before beginning any exercise program.

- **Health history.** A personal trainer should take a full health history of all clients and discuss anything that might limit the person's ability to exercise. This includes talking about what medications the client is taking, as some medicines can cause dehydration or increase blood pressure.
- **Customization.** A personal trainer assesses the client's fitness level at the beginning, and helps the client set reasonable and attainable goals with a customized workout routine.
- **Accountability.** Meeting with a personal trainer versus going to the gym or working out alone provides a layer of responsibility that can be particularly helpful for a depressed person who might have trouble getting out of bed some days. Knowing that someone is waiting for you can be motivating.

Here are some things to keep in mind when choosing a personal trainer:

- **Certification.** Today personal trainers can be certified through the American College of Sports Medicine, the Aerobic and Fitness Association of America, or the National Academy of Sports Medicine. "Looking for the gold standard of certification from a reputable organization like these three will ensure that your trainer has been properly trained," says Zak Rivera, a personal trainer with Focused Results in Lake Bluff, Illinois. "There are a lot of trainers who treat everyone the same, but especially for someone with a mental illness like depression, you want a trainer who will pay close attention to your feelings and your goals in order to empower you to be the best person you can be."

- **Trial run.** Be sure to ask for a free trial session before signing up with a personal trainer to ensure a good fit. "You want a good connection with your trainer because they will get you to a better place physically and mentally," notes Rivera.

- **Honesty.** You want someone with whom you can be honest about the workout and anything that could impact your exercise. "If you can't be honest with your personal trainer, we can't help you," says Rivera. "We want to have a dialogue with our clients in order to be in the best position to assist them in reaching their goals."

- **Environment.** Make sure the location and atmosphere of the gym is appealing to you. "When people come to our gym, we want them to feel like they're walking into their home," says Rivera. "We also don't have mirrors because we found them to be distracting to our clients in a negative way. Instead, we put up on our walls positive, inspiring, and thoughtful words to give our clients encouragement."

Overall, a personal trainer can be a great partner for depressed people in working toward their full recovery. "The key to fitness is to always keep your eyes on the end result because that will keep you moving," says Rivera.

PART III: THE TREATMENT

# CHAPTER TWENTY
## NUTRITION AND DEPRESSION

**"Maybe you have to know the darkness before you can appreciate the light."**
—Madeleine L'Engle, American author

In recent years, the role of nutrition in relation to disease and health has become more prominent, with research and studies finding that eating right can have a positive impact on overall health.

Just as nutrition is important in fighting many other types of disease, it also appears to be a key factor in preventing and healing depression. But as with medications, "the story behind diet and depression is complex."[517] Poor nutrition doesn't by itself cause the disease, but it may be a contributing factor in developing depression, and it may make existing depression worse. "A poor diet doesn't cause unipolar major depression, but inadequate nutrition can result in deficiencies of amino acids, fatty acids, vitamins, and minerals that impair your health, upset bodily processes, disturb the function and growth of brain cells, and worsen your depressive symptoms."[518]

Some medical professionals also point out that "nutrition can play a key role in the onset as well as the severity and duration of depression. Many of the easily noticeable food patterns [poor appetite, skipping meals, and a marked preference for sweets] that precede depression are the same as those that occur during depression."[519] Research has discovered several foods have a depression-fighting ability, including omega-3 fatty acids, vitamins, folate, antioxidants, amino acids, and certain minerals.

## Omega-3 Fatty Acids

Omega-3 fatty acids are essential acids found most commonly in fish oils; they play an important role in the brain's functioning processes. As a result, consuming an insufficient amount of omega-3 fatty acids may make people more prone to depression. "When our dietary fats fall out of balance, we become vulnerable to many forms of illness. Depression is one of the most common."[520] A growing body of research supports the fact that omega-3 fats *"have a potent antidepressant effect"* [emphasis in original text].[521]

Research has shown that regularly eating enough omega-3 fatty acids may help prevent and treat depression.[522] Why are omega-3 fatty acids so beneficial in the fight against depression? They reduce inflammation in the body that contributes to depression and help neurotransmitters work properly in the brain, which is crucial for maintaining mental health. Major depression elevates cytokines and eicosanoids, compounds which produce low-level inflammation in brain tissue and other areas in the body. "Antidepressants suppress this harmful activity, but so can increased levels of omega-3s, and probably more efficiently. Finally, in addition to their role in inflammatory processes, the omega-3 fatty acids are also important for proper nerve cell function. ... These fats become part of the nerve cell membrane and are important for keeping the cell and their receptors working efficiently."[523]

Depressed people may want to speak with their doctors about taking fish-oil capsules to replace essential fatty acids (EFAs), which have been found to help in recovery from the disease.[524] "The ... omega-3 fatty acids, eicosapentaenoic acid (EPA), which the body converts into docosahexanoic acid (DHA), found in fish oil, have been found to elicit antidepressant effects in humans. Many of the proposed mechanisms of this conversion involve neurotransmitters."[525]

Omega-3 fatty acids are so effective at fighting depression, in fact, that they "may be your best bet among supplements to help your fight against depression."[526] Because our bodies can't manufacture omega-3s, we must look to our diets to supply these essential fatty acids. Research has shown that omega-3 fatty acids may even increase the effectiveness of antidepressants. "Omega-3s appear to reduce inflammation and stabilize cell membranes, similar to some of the new antidepressants that are currently being tested."[527]

Another way to boost intake of omega-3 fatty acids is to follow the Mediterranean diet, which research studies has found to be effective at fighting depression. The diet of residents in the Mediterranean area uses an abundance of olive oil, which is "a rich source of monounsaturated fatty acids."[528] A study by the University of Navarra in Pamplona, Spain, linked following the Mediterranean diet with a reduced risk of depression. "The risk for becoming depressed was about twice as high in people who had the lowest adherence to the Mediterranean diet compared with those who had good or strong adherence to this dietary pattern. Other studies have found that people who eat 'Western diets' that are high in processed or 'fast foods,' meats, and other sources of saturated fats have higher rates of depression than those who eat healthier diets."[529]

Eating fish and other foods that contain omega-3 fats can help people combat depression, especially when such a diet is used in conjunction with other treatments. Fish containing high levels of omega-3s include herring, kippers, salmon, and trout; seafood with lower levels of omega-3s include scallops and shrimp. Other foods containing fatty acids are currant seed, grape seed, and walnuts.[530]

## Vitamins

Deficiencies in certain types of vitamins have been linked to depression, according to some studies. Although it's not possible to cure depression just by taking vitamins, anyone struggling with depression should try to ensure that he or she consumes the recommended daily amount of vitamins for proper brain functioning.

It makes sense to think of taking vitamins in terms of correcting deficiencies, not as a cure for disease. "Although there can be many good reasons for taking vitamins and minerals, research hasn't backed up theories that supplemental vitamins help reduce depression in people who do not have a specific vitamin deficiency. ... Deficiencies of three vitamins—folate, vitamin D, and vitamin B12—have been associated with depression in some, but not all, studies."[531] Depressed people should get their doctors' guidance to make sure they get the right type and amount of vitamins. The following vitamins may be especially helpful: A, B1, B2, B3, B6, B12, C, D, and E, as well as folate. [532]

### Folate

Extensive research has found that folate, also called folic acid, may have the most promise in treating depression. "A review of research on folate supplements conducted by Drs. [Maurizio] Fava and [David] Mischoulon at Harvard University ... found evidence for the usefulness of folate augmentation of antidepressants for residual symptoms for depression."[533]

On average, depressed people have levels of folate (which is in the B complex vitamin family) that are 25 percent lower than normal, healthy levels. Having such low folate levels has been found to be "a strong predisposing factor of poor outcome with antidepressant therapy. A controlled study has been reported to have shown that 500 mcg of folic acid enhanced the effectiveness of antidepressant medication. Folate's critical role in brain metabolic pathways has been well recognized by various researchers who have noted that depressive symptoms are the most common neuropsychiatric manifestation of folate deficiency."[534]

### Other B Vitamins

Besides folate, a variety of other B complex vitamins may prove beneficial to mental health. These B vitamins help with stress and depression, while also transforming the brain's amino acids into neurotransmitters like dopamine, norepinephrine, and serotonin. The Bs also keep one's body from developing too much homocysteine [an amino acid], which can cause inflammation.[535]

A key study about the effect of B vitamins on depression found that an increased amount of vitamin B2 and B6 improved the mood of both men and women.[536] Some medical professionals recommend depressed people "either [take] … a B-complex that contains all of the B vitamins or else [look] … for a very good multivitamin with adequate doses of B6, B12, and folic acid."[537]

## Antioxidants

The most important antioxidant (molecules that help prevent damage to the body's cells) to promote good mental health is vitamin C. Some research has tied depression "to an overly sensitive immune-system response and the excessive inflammation that results. … Antidepressants seem to work as potent anti-inflammatory drugs—but antioxidants, while less intense, have something of the same effect. They, too, help to dampen the inflammatory response, as well as protecting brain tissue."[538]

Antioxidants enhance the effectiveness of other nutrients. Omega-3 fatty acids need the protection antioxidants provide and taking a 500 milligram vitamin C supplement daily should give the needed protection.[539] A healthful diet also can ensure you get enough of this antioxidant: "Vitamin C is readily available from raw citrus fruits, strawberries, tomatoes, broccoli, and other foods. …Vitamin C is necessary for the body to produce the serotonin and norepinephrine that help prevent depression."[540]

## Vitamin D

Vitamin D, which is often added to milk, may help depression. A study done in Norway linked low vitamin D levels with depression, while those taking a vitamin D supplement found improvement with depression symptoms. "Although routine use of vitamin D for depression is not recommended, it may be a good idea to check for a deficiency in this vitamin if other therapies don't seem to be working or if you are stuck in depression."[541]

## Amino Acids

Amino acids, which the body uses to build proteins, help the brain's neurotransmitters (chemicals that transmit messages between the brain's neurons) function properly. A major contributing factor to depression is an imbalance in neurotransmitters, so it's important to consume enough amino acids regularly.

Those with depression should strive to eat a diet rich in proteins which provides amino acids. Foods such as dairy products, eggs, meats, and milk should be part of a high-quality protein diet. "Many of the neurotransmitters in the brain are made from amino acids. The neurotransmitter dopamine is made from the amino acid tyrosine and the neurotransmitter serotonin is made from the tryptophan. If there is a lack of ... these two amino acids, there will not be enough synthesis of the respective neurotransmitters, which is associated with low mood and aggression in the patients."[542]

Research into the benefits of amino acids has found that methionine, phenylalanine, tyrosine, and tryptophan provide the most benefit in treating depression, among other mood disorders.[543]

### Minerals
Consuming the proper amount of minerals is optimal for brain function. "Some minerals, including calcium and magnesium, are directly involved in processes whereby neurotransmitters affect our cells."[544] Some doctors recommend that depressed people make sure they have enough of the minerals calcium, magnesium, chromium, copper, zinc, and manganese. Other minerals that can promote good mental health include iodine, iron, lithium, and selenium.

Zinc is especially effective at fighting depression, say researchers. "At least five studies have shown that zinc levels are lower in those with clinical depression. Furthermore, intervention research shows that oral zinc can influence the effectiveness of antidepressant therapy."[545]

### Diet Versus Supplements
Although beneficial nutrients can be found naturally in foods, it's sometimes not possible for depressed people to get all the needed nutrients via diet. One of the symptoms of depression is low energy, and it takes energy to make the effort to shop for and prepare richly varied and healthful meals.[546]

"Your brain needs minerals and vitamins to process serotonin, norepinephrine, dopamine, and beta-endorphins, and to stabilize your mood and energy. Ideally, we'd get all the vitamins and minerals we need from the food we eat, but often we simply don't."[547]

Sometimes taking a multivitamin daily can close any nutrition gaps and supplementing with vitamin C, vitamin E, beta-carotene, and selenium capsules can be helpful, but check with your doctor before taking.[548] The B complex vitamins that help fight depression are included in most multivitamin supplements. When taking vitamins, keep in mind that antioxidants aren't as potent when consumed outside of their natural form, so "it is best to get antioxidants from your diet by eating a wide range of fresh fruits and vegetables, particularly those that are bright red, purple, or dark green."[549]

Nutrition plays an important role in preventing and healing depression. Those with a family history of depression or who have suffered depressive episodes should consider paying close attention to their diets to ensure they are getting the vitamins, minerals, antioxidants, folate, amino acids, and omega-3s necessary for a healthy body and mind. Family members can assist with this by making healthy meals for a depressed loved one, or by stocking the freezer with easy-to-prepare foods rich in those nutrients.

PART III: THE TREATMENT

# CHAPTER TWENTY-ONE
## PATIENTS AND DEPRESSION TREATMENT

**"Getting better from depression demands a lifelong commitment. I've made that commitment for my life's sake and for the sake of those who love me."**
—Susan Polis Schutz, American poet and co-founder of Blue Mountain Arts

Sometimes a person will put off getting treatment for depression until the disease finally incapacitates him or her, having managed until that point to function well enough to hide their depression from family and friends. Or it could be that treatment isn't working as well as it had in the past and the person is reluctant to say so, or doesn't notice.

When I first encountered depression, I just wanted to know what I had and how to get better. After a full diagnostic workup and a psych evaluation, my depression diagnosis was confirmed. Back then (more than four decades ago), the prescribed medications (lithium and other MAOIs) required twice-weekly blood tests to manage the medicines and track dosage. The side effects were very unpleasant, including constipation, dry mouth, and cravings for sweets.

The biggest thing I appreciated from that initial depression experience was that my doctors educated me about what was happening in my head. That helped me to persevere through the treatment and to trust that the doctors would work with me to overcome the depression.

Then I experienced my worst depression at 47 years old. I had been chairman of the Follett Company for two years, and prior to that position, I was vice chairman of the family business for two years. This depression lasted two years and the "go-to" medications that had worked before weren't working as effectively. I was working far below my potential; my brother and father were concerned for my health and my job. Because none of the medications were working, I slipped deeper and deeper into my depression.

That's when my brother and father talked with my doctors about trying electroconvulsive therapy (ECT). All told, I had five outpatient ECT sessions. The treatments weren't scary or anything like what movies like "One Flew Over the Cuckoo's Nest" had portrayed in such a negative fashion. As I explained earlier, before each session, I was given a twilight sedative and muscle relaxant. When I woke up from each ECT treatment, I hadn't felt a thing. (See Chapter 16 for more information on ECT treatments.)

Shortly after the final ECT treatment, something amazing happened! All the things I had learned in my personal life and all the things I learned in my business life came together. My brain was fully integrated or rewired, and I felt like smarter than I had ever been. My mind was working at warp speed—and it was wonderful! My decision to do ECT enabled me to reach new heights in my professional and personal lives.

After experiencing my new self, I realized how lucky I was. I had lost years of my adult life to depression. I made a decision to try to help other people who had mental illness by sharing my story and giving them hope. I wanted to encourage them that there is light at the end of the tunnel if you persevere through the illness with the help of your doctors, treatments, and support group of family and friends.

During my last five or six years of being chairman, I was on fire. It was like I was a different person because all my interests were different and more expanded not only in the business but in my personal life as well. The most amazing thing [ECT] had happened to me and it changed my life. It was a sharp contrast to my experience growing up.

Back then, my family had to learn alongside me about the disease and the best way to provide support during episodes of depression. My family became proficient in knowing—even when I was ranting and raving because of obsessive-compulsion or rumination—that it was part of the illness. To calm me down, they would let me rant and rave, and then help me realize that some of the things I was worried about weren't really major issues. They encouraged me to keep up with my treatment regimen. Sometimes their efforts worked and sometimes they didn't. It wasn't an easy path back then.

For others battling depression, it's important not to give up and to follow your doctors' recommendations—whether that involves medication, animal therapy, talk therapy, exercise, or other treatment. You have a responsibility in this and have to go down the pathway to recovery in a somewhat logical manner even though you're ill. I think for some people it is difficult to stay on the path, especially when they start feeling better. Sometimes people will stop taking their medications without a doctor's approval, precipitating a slide back into depression that can be even worse than the original episode.

Let me reemphasize that I believe the key to getting well when you're severely depression is to be properly diagnosed by a psychopharmacologist at a major teaching hospital. Then stick to your prescribed treatment protocol and don't stop taking meds without consulting your doctor or you could trigger a relapse.

Finally, never give up and persevere! You need to be focused and determined to beat this illness. Be open to new drug protocols and treatments if the ones you've tried don't solve your depression. Your doctors, therapists, and support groups will be there to help you. And remember: You are not alone!

PART III: THE TREATMENT

# CHAPTER TWENTY-TWO
## FAMILIES AND DEPRESSION TREATMENT

**"A lot of people don't realize that depression is an illness. I don't wish it on anyone, but if they would know how it feels, I swear they would think twice before they just shrug it off."**
—Jonathan Davis, American musician

Family members often are enormous help to those suffering from depression, but in some cases, they can be a hindrance to treatment. Sometimes family members and friends aren't helpful, not because they don't want to assist their loved one in depression treatment, but because they don't know how. Other times family members can get worn down by the cyclical nature of depression, especially if the loved one has experienced multiple episodes. Groups like the Depression and Bipolar Support Alliance, Mental Health America, and the National Alliance on Mental Illness provide both in-person and online support for families with members suffering from depression. (See the resources section on page 218 for more information.)

Family members should educated themselves about the disease and try to be as understanding as possible of the way the person acts while in the midst of an episode or depressive cycle. Here are some things to keep in mind when a family member is depressed.

**Realize depression is serious.** It's not something a person can overcome on his own. "Family members need to simply acknowledge there is a depression, that this is greater than the unpleasant mood everyone gets when there is a break up with an important person or your dog dies," says Dr. William Scheftner.

**Know it's not personal.** Someone with depression will likely seem angry and find it hard to show love to others. "Mark wasn't really Mark when he went through the depression episodes," says my sister Robin.

**Understand the disease.** Mental-health illnesses are among the most misunderstood diseases today, in large part because of the attached stigma. "It's hard for someone who hasn't experienced depression to 'get' what the disease does to a person," explains Bonnie Senner, an integrated psychodynamic therapist. "Initially, I often include the spouse and other close family members of the patient to help them gain a better understanding of depression so they can be supportive in the most beneficial way."

**Recognize the symptoms.** Just like cancer can zap a patient of strength, so depression too can make a person lethargic and unresponsive to normal things. "If you have a family member who is sad, blue, and down in the dumps, look for changes in appetite and sleep, capacity for concentration and changes in their future outlook," advises Dr. Scheftner. "When you start seeing multiple symptoms on that list, including even comments like 'I wish I were dead,' you need to make your own initial diagnosis that this is a depression that requires evaluation by a medical professional."

**Encourage treatment.** Hiding the problem won't make it go away and delaying treatment can be life-threatening if they exhibit any of the signs of suicidal thoughts (see Chapter 1 for details). Also check to make sure a loved one is following the treatment plan or taking the medication. "This can be done either by simply asking or in some cases administrating the medication itself," says Dr. Scheftner.

**Accept your limitations.** You can't make someone else's depression go away and you're not to blame for the disease. "I would get frustrated sometimes when Mark called me because I didn't know how to handle it and thought he should be talking to his doctor because I felt inadequate," says my sister Shawn.

**Get screened yourself.** Depression often runs in families. For the Litzsingers, depression had its roots in my mother's family. Of my immediate family, initially my mother and I had depression. Later some of my siblings, nieces, and nephews showed signs of depression as well. "We were battling depression on a lot of fronts [in] the family," adds Shawn.

**Have patience.** Depression can take years to recover from, even when the person is receiving treatment from doctors. "I listened to Mark as he talked over and over and over about the same thing," says Robin. "I basically kept my mouth shut and just listened."

**Don't ignore suicide threats.** "No matter how sick or tired or annoyed you are with the person's depression, never, ever condone or encourage suicide," stresses Dr. Scheftner. "To turn a person's thoughts away from suicide, list the people whose lives would be ruined and miserable forever as a result of that action—and get them professional help as soon as possible."

**Keep the person involved.** Even though it's sometimes hard for a person with depression to mingle with other people, family members should invite and encourage him into coming to events and gatherings. "Since Mark lived alone, I would bring him dinner," says my sister Heidi. "We tried to include him in things that we did as a family, be it a soccer game or whatever."

With all the progress in modern medicine, there's still a bit of mystery as to how depression impacts a person's brain, including why someone will respond wonderfully to a certain drug while another will not. "It's a difficult disease to have and to watch someone you love go through because you never know how long it will last," said my mother, Dona Litzsinger. "But even in the midst of Mark's depression, we knew we had to pull together to help him through it."

# CHAPTER TWENTY-THREE
## PATIENTS AND RECOVERY FROM DEPRESSION

"Sadness is a super important thing not to be ashamed about but to include in our lives. One of the bigger problems with sadness or depression is there's so much shame around it. If you have it you're a failure. You are felt as being very unattractive."
—Mike Mills, American musician

Depression recovery isn't easy—in fact, it will be one of the hardest things you've ever done. Unlike an injury, there's no standard protocol with a reliable expectation as to the end result. In other words, with a broken arm, the doctor would set it, tell you how many weeks you'll need a cast, prescribe a certain amount of physical therapy in some cases, then pronounce you healed. With depression, every person's experience and treatment will be different. Some recover in weeks, while some may take months or years. "In about 20 percent to 30 percent of people who have an episode of depression, the symptoms don't entirely go away."[550] That means, you might not feel normal for a long time or even remember what normal feels like.

Around 19 million Americans currently live with depression, according to the Bethesda, Maryland-based National Institute of Mental Health.[551] The institute also points out that more than 80 percent of depressed patients who receive treatment say the treatment helps.

Not getting treatment or not completing the regime of treatment your doctor prescribes can increase your chances of a relapse. Statistics from the American Psychiatric Association in Arlington, Virginia, show that at least half of those who experience a major depressive episode will have a second one, while about 80 percent of those having two episodes will have a third one.[552]

Those percentages shouldn't frighten you! Depression doesn't have to hang over your life. You have valuable information at your fingertips with this book, your doctors, family, friends, and your own experience with depression. Use it to help yourself recover and to handle any future relapses.

Don't settle for feeling merely "okay." Instead, work with therapists, and try medications and lifestyle adjustments to reclaim your happiness. We all have our ups and downs throughout our lives—it's what we learn from our challenges in life that make us stronger for the next hurdle we may encounter.

Understanding your issues clearly and charting the right course for a recovery strategy will be the roadmap to overcoming almost anything. Armed with the right tools, information, and professional help, you can create a route that is clear, organized, optimized, and focused. Be strong and ask those around you to be strong and supportive for you. Educate them like you have been educated and let them into your world to help. You would do the same for them.

Take it from someone who has lived the ups and downs of depression: you can get better and live life to the fullest. Today it is possible for anyone with depression to have a very normal life. I lost years of my adult life because of this illness, and now my job is to use this book to share resources that can help those with depression to heal quicker, faster, and better. Some things in life are worth fighting for, and we are going to fight together to get your life back on track.

## The Stages of Recovery

How a person recovers from depression is highly personal, but there are some common emotional experiences[553] many people go through. The stages of recovery are similar to the stages of grief and can include:

1. **Shock.** Many times those with depression are alarmed or surprised that they have the disease, especially when they have nothing upon which to base their understanding of what's to come.

2. **Denial.** Depressed people might have a hard time accepting this is the new "normal" for a while, especially because of continued stigma in media and culture, as well as a lack of knowledge about effective treatments.

3. **Despair.** This emotion often is a symptom of the disease as well as a reaction to the diagnosis.

4. **Anger.** A close cousin of despair, a person might feel very angry at finding out he or she suffers from depression.

5. **Acceptance.** Finally, the person comes to the place of acknowledging that this condition has its challenges but also that there's hope of a better tomorrow.

6. **Coping.** Now the person finds new ways to live, new methods of tackling the symptoms, and new habits to instill to overcome depression.

At whatever stage you are currently, remember that support is available to support you on the road to recovery. From health professionals to family and friends, there are many along the way to lend you a helping hand as you work toward a bright future free from depression.

# CHAPTER TWENTY-FOUR
## FAMILIES AND RECOVERY FROM DEPRESSION

**"If you don't think your anxiety, depression, sadness, and stress impact your physical health, think again. All of these emotions trigger chemical reactions in your body, which can lead to inflammation and a weakened immune system. Learn how to cope, sweet friend. There will always be dark days."**
—Kris Carr, American documentarian of *Crazy, Sexy Cancer*

The journey back to health from depression is often long and treacherous with setbacks along the way. This can be particular difficult when you're watching a loved one make this trip. "My compassion for my brother grew, and I wanted to be there for him in any way I could because I couldn't comprehend what that would be like to live with depression every day," says my sister Robin. "But now that he's better, it's been a pleasure to see how fun and happy he is. He's engaging with his friends; he's a wonderful sibling. You want your siblings happy, so it's a relief to know he's okay."

"When Mark finally came out of the depression, it was like my brother was back," says Todd. "When he was on the meds and battling depression, he just wasn't as present. Now it's like you just found this person that you'd lost."

My sister Heidi adds, "His experience with depression helped me with my own situational depression. It's definitely in our family. My daughter has depression. Shawn and Todd have depression. We're all on medication and doing okay, but Mark was the one who helped me find my own balance. He recommended that I talk to my doctor about depression and that made all the difference."

As my own experience shows, family and friends are vital to a person's recovery. It's so important to have their support and acceptance with a mental disease like depression because when you're in the midst of an episode, your own thinking becomes off-kilter. Once you're on the road to recovery, your support group continues to have an important role.

Here are some suggestions I have for how family and friends can help the depressed person recover:

- **Believe the person will get better.** Knowing that my family believed I would overcome this disease was fundamental to my own recovery.
- **Instill hope by telling your loved one he or she is capable of doing the hard work necessary to get better.** During recovery, family members have to walk a fine line between encouragement and criticism. "Be compassionate about what they are going through because it's a medical process and there are a lot of things they can't participate in while working on getting a good chemical balance with medications," says my sister Shawn.
- **Assist in rebuilding his or her self-image by separating out the depression symptoms from the individual's personali-ty traits.** To achieve this step, I now always recommend talk therapy with a professional as well as treatment from a psycho-pharmacologist to someone who is depressed. The combination really works well and can relieve some of the pressure on family or friends. The talk therapist can help you sort out depression issues and issues with everyday life by being a good listener and sounding board for the patient. The psychopharmacologist focuses on key indicators of how well the medication protocol is working for the patient. It's a very focused approach.
- **Adjust your communication styles when a patient is exhib-**

**iting depression symptoms.** Although the disease can be very frustrating for family and friends, remember that the patient "needs you to be in a safe, calming place," notes Shawn. "If you can't find it in your heart to be kind and helpful, then it's best to [maintain a distance]. Criticizing a person in depression is like hitting a weak dog. They take it very seriously when they are being criticized."

- **Try not to nag or push.** The support group has to walk a fine line between encouragement and pressuring. Treatment takes time, during which it's important for friends and family to be sensitive and supportive. Keep the person who is ill busy and distracted by suggesting movies, walks, and exercise. Exercise is especially helpful because it releases feel-good chemicals in the brain like endorphins. (See Chapter 19 for more on the benefits of exercise.)

- **Remember hopelessness, disinterest, anxiety, and anger are all depression symptoms.** My family was always supportive and included me in their outside activities. We went to the grocery store or walked in the park together. They patiently listened to me, even when I was ruminating and unable to break my thought process. My family was also very positive in supporting my efforts to get well. In the beginning, their care and support was instinctual because they didn't understand what I was going through. As we all educated ourselves about the disease, my family learned the best way to support me during episodes.

- **Keep up your support.** At every stage, your continued love and acceptance can be vital to the person's recovery.[554] My family continues to be very supportive of me in all my endeavors.

As the loved one moves further into recovery, family and friends can temper the person's expectations and life goals to be more realistic and reachable. Sometimes the patient might want to do too much too soon, so try to guide him or her to move forward at a slow but steady pace.

Offer support as they take on new things and have a new focus on life. I've found many new interests and hobbies over the last decade or so, including showing dogs and collecting antique cars. Since the recovery, I've had so many new interests, and my mind and life have broadened so much. I started helping entrepreneurs think through new ideas and business applications, and branched out into different industries by being an advisory board member. My new interests included politics and global affairs in this country and abroad. And I am constantly thinking of new ideas to share with the leaders of our family's company.

I also found myself more interested in helping others more. For me, it's not about race, religion, or what color your skin is—it's about being a human being and doing the right thing for each other. All the people on this planet are trying to survive and find as much happiness as possible. We all have a role to play in making each other's lives better. I believe we should strive to be good people—to be respectful, to be good listeners, to give our time to worthy causes, and to help others where we can.

One way I've tried to help others is by sharing my experience with patients, doctors, and family members in talks at Rush University Medical Center in Chicago, Illinois. After my last tough depression and recovery, I knew I was really lucky to feel so great. I approached my doctor, Dr. William Scheftner, and told him that I wanted to give back and help others with depression. I told him if Rush held public seminars on depression, I wanted to help in any way I could. I was not embarrassed by my depression and wanted to tell my story to help and inspire patients and families, encouraging depressed people to get help, stay focused, be determined, and never give up.

Dr. Scheftner introduced to me to Dr. Mark Pollack, who succeeded him as chairman of the Psychiatry Department at Rush University Medical Center and has since left. Dr. Pollack and I discussed the idea of incorporating my story into the public seminars being conducted by him and his associates at different venues in the Chicago area. Dr. Pollack liked the idea of a patient telling his story because it added an element of realism and connection. Since that time, I have spoken three times with Dr. Pollack and his wonderful staff. "In an odd, strange way, what Mark has gone through has helped a lot of people figure out what depression does," says Heidi.

I'm grateful that I've been able to use my experience with depression to help others—whether it's patients who have the disease, family members, or medical professionals. I've been blessed with a full recovery, and am now able use my knowledge and understanding to impact a wide range of people. "Mark has taught me so much, a whole world about compassion and when to use it and how to use it. We've all grown so much from this disease—in some ways it's our blessing," says Shawn. "Because every family gets hit with something, and those things that are hard are the things that really grow the family and bring the family together."

# CONCLUSION

**"A journey of a thousand miles must begin with a single step."**
—Lao Tzu, Chinese philosopher

One of the goals of this book is to make depression seem normal. That might sound strange if you have depression, but I want to normalize the disease so that people—those who have it, those with depressed family members, and the public at large—view it as a relatively "normal" disease, and for which there is treatment and hope of recovery.

Depression has a far wider reach than one would expect. In fact, "Depression will soon be the number-two illness," says Dr. Pollack. Here are some statistics that show the significant impact depression has on the world:

- 350 million: The number of people affected by some form of the disease[555]
- 16 million: Estimated number of U.S. adults with at least one major depression in 2012[556]
- 41,149: Number of suicide deaths related to depression in 2013[557]
- $80 billion: Estimated yearly cost of depression in the United States due to health-care expenses and lost productivity at work[558]
- 10 to 20 weeks: The average number of weeks for psychotherapy treatments for depression.[559]

This book has covered the many different areas of depression. It also tells the true story of my personal struggle—and that of my family—with depression. It is my hope that this book will be an important resource for patients, families, doctors, friends, and therapists to help each other in the war against this disease.

For those suffering from depression, I hope my story will inspire you to persevere and never give up hope! In my case, my journey was a roller-coaster ride over many years. There are more modern drugs today than when I was first diagnosed more than four decades ago. These newer medications have far fewer side effects and are more effective in their end results. The search continues to find better and faster ways of treating this illness. However, the brain is the last frontier in medicine and we still have a lot to learn.

Finally, here's my winning strategy for healing from depression: proper diagnosis; the right psychopharmacologist, talk therapist, and other health-care assistance; and focus, patience, and a never-give-up attitude by patients, family/friends, and doctors.

# RESOURCES

**"Every man has his secret sorrows which the world knows not; and often times we call a man cold when he is only sad."**
—Henry Wadsworth Longfellow, American poet

The following are some of the many resources available to those suffering from depression or for their families and friends. All phone numbers and websites were accurate at the time of publication.

**General Information on Depression:**
Anxiety and Depression Association of America
Silver Spring, Maryland
240-485-1001
www.adaa.org
Offers resources and information on depression.

Association of Suicide Prevention
afsp.org
Offers resources and information on preventing suicide.

Beyond Blue
www.beyondblue.org.au/
An Australian site that offers resources and information about depression, including an online live-chat option.

Mental Health America
Alexandria, Virginia
703-684-7722
800-969-6642
mhanational.org
Offers resources and information on depression.

National Alliance on Mental Illness
Arlington, Virginia
703-524-7600
800-950-6264 (helpline)
www.nami.org
Offers resources and information on depression, including a toll-free helpline.

National Institute of Mental Health
Bethesda, Maryland
1-866-615-6464 (toll-free)
www.nimh.nih.gov/site-info/contact-nimh.shtml
Offer resources and information on depression, including an online live-chat option.

Suicide Prevention Hotlines
800-SUICIDE (800-784-2433)
800-273-TALK (800-273-8255)
800-799-4889 (for the hearing impaired)

**Animal Therapy**
Alliance of Therapy Dogs
Cheyenne, Wyoming
877-843-7364
www.therapydogs.com
Provides support to members involved in animal-assisted activities.

American Kennel Club
New York, New York
212-696-8200
www.akc.org/events/title-recognition-program/therapy/organizations/
Offers a list of therapy-dog organizations across the United States.

Pet Partners
Bellevue, Washington 425-679-5500
Petpartners.org
Provides animal-assisted therapy, activities, and education.

Saratoga WarHorse
Saratoga Springs, NY
518-886-8131
www.saratogawarhorse.com
Offers veterans a three-day experience that has proven to be effective and invaluable for those struggling to adjust to life after military service.

**Nutritionists**
Academy of Nutrition and Dietetics
www.eatright.org
www.eatright.org/find-an-expert
Has a find-an-expert search option for registered dietitians and nutritionists on its website.

American Nutrition Association
theana.org
https://portal.theana.org/s/professional-directory-list
Offers a find-a-practitioner search on its website.

National Association of Nutrition Professionals
Sacramento, California
209-224-0003

www.nanp.org
nanp.org/find-a-practitioner/
Provides a list of board-certified holistic-nutrition members.

**Personal Trainers**
Pure Gym
puregym.com/blog/mental-health-the-gym/
Offers articles about the gym and mental health.

**Therapists**
Good Therapy
888-563-2112, ext. 1
www.goodtherapy.org
Offers a nationwide directory of therapists.

Other therapist sites:
https://www.psychologytoday.com/us/therapists

https://locator.apa.org/

https://www.betterhelp.com/therapists/

https://adaa.org/netforum/findatherapist

**Further Reading Suggestions**
Research into depression continues to generate new ideas and studies. Here are some articles and books for additional reading on the subject.

"Brain Training for Anxiety, Depression and Other Mental Conditions" by Andrea Petersen. *The Wall Street Journal.* 18 January 2016. http://www.wsj.com/articles/brain-training-for-anxiety-depression-and-other-mental-conditions-1453144315. Accessed 2/10/21.

"Chicago's Mental Health 'Crisis': Is Reform of Police Enough?" by Jason

Thomson. *Christian Science Monitor*. 29 January 2016. http://www. csmonitor.com/USA/Justice/2016/0129/Chicago-s-mental-health-crisis-Is-reform-of-police-enough. Accessed 2/10/21.

*Darkness Visible: A Memoir of Madness* by William Styron (Random House, 1990). From the Amazon.com description: "A work of great personal courage and a literary tour de force, this bestseller is Styron's true account of his descent into a crippling and almost suicidal depression. Styron is perhaps the first writer to convey the full terror of depression's psychic landscape, as well as the illuminating path to recovery."

"Hayden Panettiere Returns to Work Following Battle with Postpartum Depression." Yahoo News. 10 January 2016. https://www.yahoo.com/news/hayden-panettiere-returns-to-work-following-battle-134443339. html. Accessed 2/10/21.

"Hot Wired for Happiness?" by Amy Ellis Nutt. *The Washington Post*. 3 March 2016. http://www.washingtonpost.com/sf/national/2016/03/03/brain-hacking-hot-wired-for-happiness/. Accessed 2/10/21

*Man's Search for Meaning* by Viktor E. Frankl. From the Amazon.com description: "Psychiatrist Viktor Frankl's memoir has riveted generations of readers with its descriptions of life in Nazi death camps and its lessons for spiritual survival."

"Panel Calls for Depression Screenings During and After Pregnancy" by Pam Belluck. *The New York Times*. 26 January 2016. http://mobile.nytimes. com/2016/01/27/health/post-partum-depression-test-epds-screening-guidelines.html. Accessed 2/10/21.

Posttraumatic Stress Syndrome information. https://www.ptsd.va.gov/understand/index.asp. Accessed 2/10/2021.

"Solutions for Stressed-Out High-School Students" by Nikhil Goyal.

*The Wall Street Journal.* 12 February 2016. http://www.wsj.com/articles/solutions-for-stressed-out-high-school-students-1455301683.   Accessed 2/10/21.

"Villanova's Game-Winner: Why We Watch Sports" by Jason Gay. *The Wall Street Journal.* 5 April 2016. http://www.wsj.com/articles/villanovas-game-winner-why-we-watch-sports-1459870607. Accessed 2/10/21.

"'You're Not Alone!' We're Starting a Conversation about Anxiety, Depression, Help and Hope." *Oprah Magazine.* February 2016.

**Inspirational Viewings**
I put these under the "never-give-up" and encouraging category.

"Bretagne—Dog's Best Day." https://www.youtube.com/embed/ezcHy8DkrmE?rel=0. Accessed 2/10/21.

"God Bless the USA" performance by the Texas Tenors. https://www.youtube.com/watch?v=daqwGRdRIsk. Accessed 2/10/21.

"So God Made a Dog." http://videos2view.net/God-made-a-dog.htm. Accessed 2/10/21.

"TCU Erases 31-point Deficit to Beat Oregon in 3OT in Valero Alamo Bowl." 3 January 2016. http://espn.go.com/college-football/recap?gameId=400852741. Accessed 2/10/21.

# BIBLIOGRAPHY

**"There are far, far better things ahead than anything we leave behind."**
—C. S. Lewis, British writer

**Articles**
Abate, Carolyn. "The Best Depression Apps of the Year." Healthline.com. 18 May 2017. http://www.healthline.com/health/depression/top-iphone-android-apps#2. Accessed 2/10/21.

Alavi, S. S.; M. R. Maracy, F. Jannatifard, & M. Eslami. (2011). The effect of psychiatric symptoms on the internet addiction disorder in Isfahan University students. Journal of Research in Medical Sciences: The Official Journal of Isfahan University of Medical Sciences, 16(6), 793–800. https://www.ncbi.nlm.nih.gov/pmc/articles/PMC3214398/#:~:text=Excessive%20Internet%20use%20may%20create,low%20family%20relationships%20and%20anxiety. Accessed 2/22/21.

Alexander, Donovan. "Technology Addiction: When is Technology Too Much?" 16 August 2020. https://interestingengineering.com/technology-addiction-when-is-technology-too-much. Accessed 2/13/21.

"Antidepressants for Children and Teens." MayoClinic.org. http://

www.mayoclinic.org/diseases-conditions/teen-depression/in-depth/antidepressants/ART-20047502. Accessed 2/10/21.

Asa, Richard. "Dangers of Helicopter Parenting When Your Kids Are Teens." Chicago Tribune.com. 23 June 2015. http://www.chicagotribune.com/lifestyles/sc-fam-0630-teen-helicopter-parent-20150623-story.html. Accessed 2/10/21.

Azar, Adnan. "Five Ways AI Can Help Revolutionize Mental Healthcare." Forbes.com. 19 August 2020. https://www.forbes.com/sites/forbestechcouncil/2020/08/19/five-ways-ai-can-help-revolutionize-mental-healthcare/?sh=4c646ca513ab. Accessed 2/26/21.

Bakker, David, Nikolaos Kazantzis, Debra Rickwood, and Nikki Rickard. "Mental Health Smartphone Apps: Review and Evidence-Based Recommendations for Future Developments." JMIR Mental Health. 2016 Jan-Mar. 3(1): e7. Published online 1 March 2016. https://www.ncbi.nlm.nih.gov/pmc/articles/PMC4795320. Accessed 2/10/21.

Banducci, Sarah. "Mobile Device Addiction Linked to Depression, Anxiety." Science Daily.com. 2 March 2016. https://www.sciencedaily.com/releases/2016/03/160302121325.htm. Accessed 2/13/21.

Barron, Daniel. "The Rise of Big Data Psychiatry." *The Wall Street Journal.* 29 April 2021. https://www.wsj.com/articles/the-rise-of-big-data-psychiatry-11619704849. Accessed 5/7/21.

Bergland, Christopher. "Parental Warmth Is Crucial for a Child's Well-Being: Toxic Childhood Stress Alters Neural Responses Linked to Illness in Adulthood." PsychologyToday.com. 4 October 2013. https://www.psychologytoday.com/blog/the-athletes-way/201310/parental-warmth-is-crucial-child-s-well-being. Accessed 2/10/21.

Bobinchock, Adriana. "New Treatment for Depression Shows Immediate

Results." *Harvard Gazette.* 28 July 2014. http://news.harvard.edu/gazette/ story/2014/07/new-treatment-for-depression-shows-immediate-results. Accessed 2/10/21.

Bocanegra, Juan. "Mental Health: A Problem We Need to Take Care of in Latin America." *Latin American Post.* 6 April 2019. https:// latinamericanpost.com/27444-mental-health-a-problem-we-need-to-take-care-of-in-latin-america. Accessed 3/20/21.

Borresen, Kelsey. "Artist Channels How Depression Feels Into Beautiful Drawings." *Huffington Post* Healthy Living. 11 August 2017. http:// www.huffingtonpost.com/entry/artist-depression-illustrations_ us_598cd864e4b090964295eef3?ncid=APPLENEWS00001. Accessed 2/10/21.

Buhr, Sarah. "Huddle Is a Mental Health App that Aims to be a Safe Space to Share with Peers." Techcrunch.com. 15 August 2017. https:// techcrunch.com/2017/08/15/huddle-is-a-mental-health-app-that-aims-to-be-a-safe-space-to-share-with-peers/amp/. Accessed 2/10/21.

Cha, Ariana Eunjung. "More than a Third of Teenage Girls Experience Depression, New Study Says." *The Washington Post.* 31 May 2017. https://www.washingtonpost.com/news/to-your-health/wp/2017/05/31/ more-than-a-third-of-teenage-girls-experience-depression-new-study-says/?utm_term=.c4a7dd6223ca. Accessed 2/10/21.

Chee KY, et al. "Country Variations in Depressive Symptoms Profile in Asian Countries: Findings of the Research on Asia Psychotropic Prescription (REAP) Studies." Asia-Pacific Psychiatry. 2015 Sep;7(3):276-85. doi: 10.1111/appy.12170. Epub 13 January 2015. PMID: 25641910. https://pubmed.ncbi.nlm.nih.gov/25641910/. Accessed 3/20/21.

Chen, Jennifer. "How New Ketamine Drug Helps with Depression." Yale Medicine.org. 21 March 2019. https://www.yalemedicine.org/news/

ketamine-depression. Accessed 2/26/21.

Cherry, Kendra. "The Health Consequences of Loneliness: Causes and Health Consequences of Feeling Lonely." Verywellmind.com. 23 March 2020. https://www.verywellmind.com/loneliness-causes-effects-and-treatments-2795749. Accessed 2/5/21.

Clarke, Jodi. "Can Artificial Intelligence Help with Depression?" Very Well Mind.com. https://www.verywellmind.com/can-artificial-intelligence-help-depression-4158330. Accessed 2/27/21.

Conner, Kenneth R., et al. "Meta-analysis of depression and substance use among individuals with alcohol use disorders." *Journal of Substance Abuse Treatment,* Vol. 37,2 (2009): 127-37. doi:10.1016/j.jsat.2008.11.007. https://www.ncbi.nlm.nih.gov/pmc/articles/PMC4864601/. Accessed 3/5/21.

"COVID-19 and Your Mental Health." MayoClinic.org. 15 October 2020. https://www.mayoclinic.org/diseases-conditions/coronavirus/in-depth/mental-health-covid-19/art-20482731. Accessed 2/5/21.

"COVID-19 Has Produced 'Alarming' Increase in Loneliness." Medical News Today.com. 25 November 2020. https://www.medicalnewstoday.com/articles/alarming-covid-19-study-shows-80-of-respondents-report-significant-symptoms-of-depression. Accessed 2/5/21.

DeRubeis, Robert J.; Greg J. Siegle, and Steven D. Hollon. "Cognitive Therapy versus Medications for Depression: Treatment Outcomes and Neural Mechanisms." *Nature Reviews Neuroscience.* Nature.com. October 2008. 788–796. https://doi.org/10.1038/nrn2345. Accessed 2/10/21.

Dennon, Anne. "Coronavirus Impacts on Students and Online Learning." 15 December 2020, BestColleges.com. https://www.bestcolleges.com/blog/coronavirus-impacts-on-students. Accessed 2/2/21.

"Depression." Pan American Health Organization. https://www.paho.org/en/topics/depression. Accessed 3/20/21.

"Depression." Sane.org. 21 May 2001. https://www.sane.org/information-stories/facts-and-guides/depression. Accessed 3/20/21.

"Depression." World Health Organization. 30 January 2020. https://www.who.int/news-room/fact-sheets/detail/depression. Accessed 3/30/21.

"Depression and Addiction." DualDiagnosis.org. https://dualdiagnosis.org/depression-and-addiction. Accessed 3/5/21.

"Depression Facts." U.S. Centers for Disease Control and Prevention website. http://www.cdc.gov/nchs/fastats/depression.htm. Accessed 2/10/21.

"Depression in Children and Teens." *American Academy of Child & Adolescent Psychiatry*. No. 4; Updated October 2018. http://www.aacap.org/AACAP/Families_and_Youth/Facts_for_Families/FFF-Guide/The-Depressed-Child-004.aspx. Accessed 2/10/21.

"Depression in Europe: Facts and Figures." World Health Organization. https://www.euro.who.int/en/health-topics/noncommunicable-diseases/mental-health/news/news/2012/10/depression-in-europe/depression-in-europe-facts-and-figures. Accessed 3/20/21.

"Depression (Major Depressive Disorder)." MayoClinic.org. 3 February 2018. https://www.mayoclinic.org/diseases-conditions/depression/symptoms-causes/syc-20356007. Accessed 2/10/21.

"Depression Recovery: An Overview." WebMD.com. 27 September 2020. http://www.webmd.com/depression/recovery-overview. Accessed 2/10/21.

Dewey, Caitlin. "A Stunning Map of Depression Rates around the World." *The Washington Post*. 7 November 2013. https://www.washingtonpost. com/news/worldviews/wp/2013/11/07/a-stunning-map-of-depression-rates-around-the-world/. Accessed 3/30/21.

Diamond, Stephen A., Ph.D. "The Psychology of Psychopharmacology." PsychologyToday.com. 18 April 2008. https://www.psychologytoday.com/ blog/evil-deeds/200804/the-psychology-psychopharmacology. Accessed 2/10/21.

Doheny, Kathleen. "Pets for Depression and Health: Can Your Depression Problems Improve When You Interact with Your Pet?" WebMD.com. 3 August 2012.

Dryden-Edwards, Roxanne, MD. "Teen Depression: 10 Warning Signs for Teen Suicide." MedicineNet.com. http://www.medicinenet.com/teen_ depression/article.htm. Accessed 2/16/21.

Ducharme, Jamie. "COVID-19 is Making America's Loneliness Epidemic Even Worse." Time.com. 8 May 2020. https://time.com/5833681/ loneliness-covid-19. Accessed 2/5/21.

"Electroconvulsive Therapy (ECT)." MayoClinic.org. 25 October 2012. http://www.mayoclinic.org/tests-procedures/electroconvulsive-therapy/ basics/definition/PRC-20014161. Accessed 2/16/21.

"The Facts." Beyond Blue.org. https://www.beyondblue.org.au/the-facts. Accessed 3/20/21.

"Family and Friends' Guide to Recovery from Depression and Bipolar Disorder." Depression and Bipolar Support Alliance. 2006.

"FDA Approves First Treatment for Postpartum Depression." FDA.gov. 19

March 2019. https://www.fda.gov/news-events/press-announcements/fda-approves-first-treatment-post-partum-depression. Accessed 2/26/21.

Fink, M. "What Was Learned: Studies by the Consortium for Research in ECT (CORE) 1997–2011." U.S. National Library of Medicine National Institutes of Health, 129(6), pp. 417-26. 12 February 2014. http://www.ncbi.nlm.nih.gov/pubmed/24571807. Accessed 2/16/21.

Fontana, Francesca. "Some Companies Want You to Take a Mental-Health Day." *The Wall Street Journal.* 15 August 2017. https://www.wsj.com/articles/why-some-companies-want-you-to-take-a-mental-health-day-1502789400. Accessed 2/16/21.

Garcia-Navarro, Lulu. "The Risk of Teen Depression and Suicide is Linked to Smartphone Use, Study Says." NPR.org. 17 December 2017. https://www.npr.org/2017/12/17/571443683/the-call-in-teens-and-depression. Accessed 2/22/21.

Gberie, Lansana. "Mental Illness: Invisible but Devastating." *Africa Renewal.* December 2016-March 2017. https://www.un.org/africarenewal/magazine/december-2016-march-2017/mental-illness-invisible-devastating. Accessed 3/20/21.

"Gene Therapy for Depression: A Futuristic Treatment." MentalHealthDaily.com. http://mentalhealthdaily.com/2015/08/21/gene-therapy-for-depression-a-futuristic-treatment/. Accessed 2/16/21.

"Genetic Variation Linked to Response to Anxiety Could Inform Personalized Therapies." Science Daily.com. 2 July 2019. https://www.sciencedaily.com/releases/2019/07/190702112813.htm. Accessed 2/18/21.

Glatter, Robert. "Digital Addiction: A Recipe for Isolation, Depression and Anxiety." Forbes.com. 30 April 2018. https://www.forbes.com/sites/robertglatter/2018/04/13/digital-addiction-a-recipe-for-isolation-depression-and-anxiety/?sh=364452bb5f6b. Accessed 2/20/21.

Goldberg, Emma. "Teens in Covid Isolation: 'I Felt Like I Was Suffocating.'" *The New York Times.* 12 November 2020. https://www. nytimes.com/2020/11/12/health/covid-teenagers-mental-health.html. Accessed 2/16/21.

Gordon, Joshua, M.D. "New Hope for Treatment-Resistant Depression: Guessing Right on Ketamine." National Institute of Mental Health. NIMH.gov. 13 August 2019. https://www.nimh.nih.gov/about/director/ messages/2019/new-hope-for-treatment-resistant-depression-guessing-right-on-ketamine.shtml. Accessed 2/26/21.

Gordon, Sherri. "Why Mental Health Disorders Co-Exist with Substance Abuse." Verywellmind.com. 16 January 2021. https://www.verywellmind. com/co-occurring-disorders-mental-health-and-addiction-4158280. Accessed 3/5/21.

Greenlaw, Ellen. "Getting Started: Talk Therapy for Depression." WebMD. com. 6 July 2010. http://www.webmd.com/depression/features/therapy-therapist. Accessed 2/16/21.

Groberman, Alex. "Shock Treatments for Depression." PsyWeb.com. 23 May 2012.

Grohol, John M., Psy.D. "Alternative Treatments for Depression." PsychCentral.com.

Hadler, Nicole. "Coping with the COVID-19 Pandemic as a College Student." University of Michigan.edu. https://medicine.umich.edu/dept/ psychiatry/michigan-psychiatry-resources-covid-19/adults-specific-resources/coping-covid-19-pandemic-college-student. Accessed 2/2/21.

Hall-Flavin, Daniel K. "Natural Remedies for Depression: Are They

Effective?" MayoClinic.org. 11 September 2018 http://www.mayoclinic. org/diseases-conditions/depression/expert-answers/natural-remedies-for-depression/faq-20058026. Accessed 2/18/21.

Harrison, Rachel. "Drinking During COVID-19 Up Among People with Anxiety and Depression." New York University School of Global Public Health. 19 January 2021. https://www.nyu.edu/about/news-publications/news/2021/january/alcohol-use-covid-19.html. Accessed 3/5/21.

Hendriksen, Ellen, Ph.D. "Is Your Gut Making You Depressed or Anxious?" QuickandDirtyTips.com. 6 April 2018. http://www.quickanddirtytips. com/health-fitness/mental-health/is-your-gut-making-you-depressed-or-anxious. Accessed 2/18/21.

"Historical Understandings of Depression." MentalHelp.net. www. mentalhelp.net/articles/historical-understandings-of-depression. Accessed 2/18/21.

Holland, Kimberly. "Understanding the Link Between Alcohol Use and Depression." Healthline.com. 25 June 2019. https://www.healthline.com/health/mental-health/alcohol-and-depression. Accessed 3/5/21.

Holmes, Lindsay. "11 Statistics that Will Change the Way You Think about Depression." *The Huffington Post.* 21 January 2015. http://www. huffingtonpost.com/2015/01/20/depression-statistics_n_6480412.html. Accessed 2/18/21.

Huizen, Jennifer. "What to Know about Mental Health Stigma in Latin America." Medical News Today. 27 January 2021. https://www. medicalnewstoday.com/articles/mental-health-stigma-in-latin-america. Accessed 3/20/21.

Hurley, Dan. "The Return of Electroshock Therapy." *The Atlantic.* December 2015. http://www.theatlantic.com/magazine/archive/2015/12/

the-return-of-electroshock-therapy/413179/. Accessed 2/18/21.

Itkowitz, Colby. "Finding Hope on a Park Bench." *The Washington Post.* 18 July 2017. E1.

Jansson, Asa. "Mood Disorders and the Brain: Depression, Melancholia, and the Historiography of Psychiatry." Cambridge University Press and U.S. National Library of Medicine, National Institutes of Health. July 2011, 55(3) pp. 393-99. www.ncbi.nlm.nih.gov/pmc/articles/PMC3143872/. Accessed 2/18/21.

Jargon, Julie. "Lonely Girls: How the Pandemic Has Deepened the Isolation of Adolescents." *The Wall Street Journal.* 29 July 2020. https://www.wsj.com/articles/lonely-girls-how-the-pandemic-has-deepened-the-isolation-of-adolescents-11595937600. Accessed 2/5/21.

John, Arit. "Increased Anxiety and Depression Top College Students' Concerns in Coronavirus Survey." 25 March 2020. *The Los Angeles Times.* https://www.latimes.com/california/story/2020-03-25/college-students-anxiety-depression-coronavirus-survey. Accessed 2/2/21.

Kelly, Kate. "How Loneliness Can Impact Kids with Learning and Attention Issues." Understood.org. https://www.understood.org/en/friends-feelings/managing-feelings/loneliness-sadness-isolation/how-loneliness-can-impact-kids-with-learning-and-attention-issues. Accessed 2/18/21.

Kirsch, Irving, M.D. "Antidepressants and the Placebo Effect." *Zeitschrift fur Psychologie (Journal of Psychology)*, Hogrefe Publishing. 28 February 2015. Vol. 222, Issue 3. 128–134. http://econtent.hogrefe.com/doi/abs/10.1027/2151-2604/a000176. Accessed 2/18/21.

Kluger, Jeffrey. "New Clues to Depression Spotted in the Genome." Time.com. 1 August 2016. http://time.com/4431292/depression-genome/. Accessed 2/18/21.

Knapton, Sarah. "Depression Is a Physical Illness Which Could Be Treated with Anti-inflammatory Drugs, Scientists Suggest." *The Telegraph.* 8 September 2017. http://www.telegraph.co.uk/science/2017/09/08/depression-physical-illness-could-treated-anti-inflammatory. Accessed 2/18/21.

"Lack of Parental Support during Childhood Is Associated with Increased Adult Depression and Chronic Health Problems, Study Finds." American Psychological Association. 21 March 2004. http://www.apa.org/news/press/releases/2004/03/parental-support.aspx. Accessed 2/18/21.

Landau, Elizabeth. "Dogs First Domesticated in Europe, Study Says." CNN Health. 14 November 2013. http://www.cnn.com/2013/11/14/health/dogs-domesticated-europe. Accessed 2/18/21.

Lalayants, Marina, and Jonathan D. Prince. "Loneliness and Depression or Depression-Related Factors among Child Welfare-Involved Adolescent Females." *Child and Adolescent Social Work Journal.* April 2015, Volume 32, Issue 2. https://link.springer.com/article/10.1007/s10560-014-0344-6. Accessed 2/18/21.

Levine, David. "A Look at Depression Around the World." *U.S. News and World Report.* 7 July 2017. https://health.usnews.com/health-care/patient-advice/articles/2017-07-07/a-look-at-depression-around-the-world. Accessed 3/30/21.

Lien, Tracey. "Depressed But Can't See a Therapist? This Chatbot Could Help." *The Los Angeles Times.* 23 August 2017. http://www.latimes.com/business/technology/la-fi-tn-woebot-20170823-htmlstory.html. Accessed 2/18/21.

"Helping Young Adult Children Cope with Depression." Mental Health Treatment.net. http://mentalhealthtreatment.net/helping-young-adult-children-cope-with-depression. Accessed 2/18/21.

Lythcott-Haims, Julie. "Kids of Helicopter Parents Are Sputtering Out." *How to Raise an Adult: Break Free of the Overparenting Trap and Prepare Your Kid for Success*, excerpt on Slate.com. 5 July 2015. http://www. slate.com/articles/double_x/doublex/2015/07/helicopter_parenting_is_ increasingly_correlated_with_college_age_depression.html. Accessed 2/18/21.

"Major Depression among Adolescents." National Institute of Mental Health, National Institutes of Health. https://www.nimh.nih.gov/health/ statistics/prevalence/major-depression-among-adolescents.shtml. Accessed 2/18/21.

"Managing Loneliness During COVID-19." Sharp Mesa Vista Hospital. 8 September 2020. https://www.sharp.com/health-news/managing-loneliness-during-covid-19.cfm. Accessed 2/5/21.

Mayton, Rosie, et al. "Explanatory models of depression in sub-Saharan Africa: Synthesis of qualitative evidence." *Social Science & Medicine*. vol. 246. February 2020. DOI: 10.1016j.socscimed.2019.112760, https://www. sciencedirect.com/science/article/pii/S0277953619307555. Accessed 3/20/21.

McClurg, Lesley. "Pandemic Takes Toll on Children's Mental Health." NPR. org. 28 November 2020. https://www.npr.org/2020/11/28/938460892/ pandemic-takes-toll-on-childrens-mental-health. Accessed 2/2/21.

McMillen, Matt. "Ketamine: The Future of Depression Treatment?" WebMd.com. 23 September 2014. http://www.webmd.com/depression/ news/20140923/ketamine-depression#1. Accessed 2/18/21.

"Mental Health During COVID-19: Signs Your Child May Need More Support." Healthy Children.org. 23 October 2021. https://www.

healthychildren.org/English/health-issues/conditions/COVID-19/Pages/ Signs-your-Teen-May-Need-More-Support.aspx. Accessed 2/2/21.

"Mental Health Providers: Tips on Finding One." MayoClinic.org. 16 May 2017. http://www.mayoclinic.org/diseases-conditions/mental-illness/in-depth/mental-health-providers/art-20045530. Accessed 2/18/21.

Miller, Caroline. "Is Internet Addiction Real?" Child Mind.org, accessed February 13, 2021. https://childmind.org/article/is-internet-addiction-real/. Accessed 2/13/21.

Miranda, D.; B. Athanasio, A. Oliveira, & A. Simeos-e-Silva. "How is the COVID-19 Pandemic Impacting Mental Health of Children and Adolescents?" NIH.gov. 10 September 2020. DOI: 10.1016/j. ijdrr.2020.101845. Accessed 2/22/21.

Mitchell, Heidi. "To Treat Depression, Start with a Digital Therapist." *The Wall Street Journal*. 26 June 2017. R13.

Morris, Betsy. "Quarantining the Elderly is Harmful to their Health." *The Wall Street Journal*. 21 July 2020.

Morris, Nathaniel. "Should People without Depression Take Medication to Prevent It?" *The Washington Post*. 17 September 2017. https://www. washingtonpost.com/national/health-science/should-people-without-depression-take-medication-to-prevent-it/2017/09/15/92623856-619b-11e7-a4f7-af34fc1d9d39_story.html?utm_term=.046f6f8aa244. Accessed 2/18/21.

Nauert, Rick, Ph.D. "Long-Term Use of Opioids Ups Risk for Depression." PsychCentral.com. 13 January 2016.

Nelson, Jeff. "JoJo Reveals Clinical Depression Diagnosis: 'Sometimes We Just Need a Little Help.'" *People Magazine*. 29 April 2020. https://

people.com/music/jojo-clinical-depression-family-addiction-struggles. Accessed 3/26/21.

Newport, Frank. "Most U.S. Smartphone Owners Check Phone at Least Hourly." Gallup.com. 9 July 2015. https://news.gallup.com/poll/184046/smartphone-owners-check-phone-least-hourly.aspx. Accessed 2/13/21.

Nierenberg, Cari. "7 Ways to Recognize Depression in 20-Somethings." Live Science.com. 27 October 2016. https://www.livescience.com/56602-signs-depression-young-adults.html. Accessed 2/18/21.

Nogrady, Bianca. "Antidepressant Approvals Could Herald New Era in Psychiatric Drugs." The-Scientist.com. 1 October 2019. https://www.the-scientist.com/bio-business/antidepressant-approvals-could-herald-new-era-in-psychiatric-drugs-66475. Accessed 2/26/21.

Nolan, Lucas. "Elon Musk Claims His Brain Chip Will Cure Depression, Addiction." Breitbart.com. 13 July 2020. https://www.breitbart.com/tech/2020/07/13/elon-musk-claims-his-brain-chip-will-cure-depression-addiction/. Accessed 3/5/21.

Oaklander, Mandy. "The Anti Antidepressant." *Time*. 7 August 2017. 38–45.

Odgers, C. & M.B. Robb. *Tweens, Teens, Tech, and Mental Health: Coming of Age in an Increasingly Digital, Uncertain, and Unequal World, 2020*. San Francisco, California: Common Sense Media, 2020. https://www.commonsensemedia.org/sites/default/files/uploads/pdfs/tweens-teens-tech-and-mental-health-full-report-final-for-web1.pdf. Accessed 2/13/21.

Petersen, Andrea. "The Struggle to Cope With Depression Amid Coronavirus." *The Wall Street Journal*. 12 April 2020. https://www.wsj.com/articles/the-struggle-to-cope-with-depression-amid-coronavirus-11586696401. Accessed 2/5/21.

Petroff, Alanna. "Google is Offering a Test for Depression." CNN. 24 August 2017. http://money.cnn.com/2017/08/24/technology/google-depression-questionnaire/index.html. Accessed 2/16/21.

Phillips, Michael. "Army Tests Injection for PTSD." *The Wall Street Journal.* 12 June 2017. https://www.wsj.com/articles/can-a-single-injection-conquer-ptsd-the-army-wants-to-find-out-1497279572?mg=prod/accounts-wsj. Accessed 2/18/21.

Pinker, Susan. "The Science of Staying Connected." *The Wall Street Journal.* 2 April 2020. https://www.wsj.com/articles/the-science-of-staying-connected-11585835999. Accessed 2/5/21.

Pogosyan, Marianna. "How Culture Affects Depression." *Psychology Today.* 6 December 2017. https://www.psychologytoday.com/us/blog/between-cultures/201712/how-culture-affects-depression. Accessed 3/30/21.

"Poor Mental Health, An Obstacle to Development in Latin America." World Bank.org. 13 July 2015. https://www.worldbank.org/en/news/feature/2015/07/13/bad-mental-health-obstacle-development-latin-america. Accessed 3/20/21.

Rao, Murali, MD, and Julie M. Alderson, DO. "New Depression Treatments Reported." Science Daily.com. February 2014. www.sciencedaily.com/releases/2014/02/140214130719. Accessed 2/18/21.

Rao, T.S. Sathyanarayana; M.R. Asha, B.N. Ramesh, & K.S. Jagannatha Rao. "Understanding Nutrition, Depression and Mental Illnesses." IndianJPsychiatry.com. April–June 2008. http://www.ncbi.nlm.nih.gov/pmc/articles/PMC2738337. Accessed 2/18/21.

Raypole, Crystal. "Loneliness and Depression: What's the Connection?" Healthline.com. 2 July 2020. https://www.healthline.com/health/loneliness-and-depression. Accessed 2/5/21.

"Recognize the Warning Signs of Suicide." WebMD. September 2012. http://www.webmd.com/depression/guide/depression-recognizing-signs-of-suicide#3. Accessed 2/18/21.

"Recovering from a Mental Health Condition." Beyondblue.org. https://www.beyondblue.org.au/get-support/recovery-and-staying-well. Accessed 2/18/21.

Reinberg, Steven. "Addictive Internet Use Tied to Depression in Teens." HealthDay News on Medicine Net.com. 2 August 2020. https://www.medicinenet.com/script/main/art.asp?articlekey=118570. Accessed 2/22/21.

Rothkopf, Joanna. "Autopsy: Robin Williams Had Lewy Body Dementia." Salon.com. 13 November 2014. http://www.salon.com/2014/11/13/autopsy_robin_williams_had_lewy_body_dementia. Accessed 2/20/21.

Ruiz, Rebecca. "Finally, We're Talking about Mental Illness Like Adults." Mashable.com. 13 August 2014. http://mashable.com/2014/08/13/robin-williams-mental-health-stigma/#yg3qCXjFa8qW. Accessed 2/20/21.

Sanders, Laura. "Microbes Can Play Games with the Mind." Science News.org. 23 March 2016. https://www.sciencenews.org/article/microbes-can-play-games-mind. Accessed 2/20/21.

Sandoiu, Ana. "Depression: Gene-Activating Drug Reverses Symptoms in Mice." *Medical News Today*. 19 February 2019. https://www.medicalnewstoday.com/articles/324492. Accessed 2/18/21.

Sankoh, Osman; Stephen Sevalie, and Mark Weston. "Mental Health in

Africa." *The Lancet,* Vol. 6, issue 9, E954-E955. 1 September 2018. DOI: 10.1016/S2214-109X(18)30303-6, https://www.thelancet.com/journals/langlo/article/PIIS2214-109X(18)30303-6/fulltext. Accessed 3/20/21.

Scaccia, Annamarya. "Could Party Drug Ketamine Be a Treatment for Depression?" Rolling Stone.com. 21 June 2017. http://www.rollingstone.com/culture/features/ketamine-future-of-depression-treatment-w488998. Accessed 2/20/21.

Schiffrin, Holly H., et al. "Helping or Hovering? The Effects of Helicopter Parenting on College Students' Well-Being." *Journal of Child and Family Studies.* April 2014, Volume 23, Issue 3, 548–557. https://doi.org/10.1007/s10826-013-9716-3. Accessed 2/20/21.

Schmidt, Charles. "Mental Health May Depend on Creatures in the Gut." *Scientific American.* 1 March 2015. https://www.scientificamerican.com/article/mental-health-may-depend-on-creatures-in-the-gut/?print=true. Accessed 2/20/21.

Scott, Larissa. "Doctors Worry as Mental Health Issues with Children Increase During Pandemic." ABC Action News. 29 December 2020. https://www.abcactionnews.com/rebound/coronavirus-stress/doctors-worry-as-mental-health-issues-with-children-increase-during-pandemic. Accessed 2/2/21.

Seppala, Emma. "Eight Ways to Ease the Pain of Loneliness." The Greater Good Science Center. 2 October 2020. https://greatergood.berkeley.edu/article/item/eight_ways_to_ease_the_pain_of_loneliness. Accessed 2/5/21.

Serani, Deborah, Psy.D. "Genetic Testing for Better Depression Treatment." *Psychology Today.* 1 July 2014. https://www.psychologytoday.com/blog/two-takes-depression/201407/genetic-testing-better-depression-treatment. Accessed 2/20/21.

"Service Animals and Assisted-Animal Therapy." *reSearch*, Vol. 8, Issue 1. National Rehabilitation Information Center. http://www.naric. com/?q=en/publications/volume-8-issue-1-service-animals-and-assisted-animal-therapy. Accessed 2/20/21.

Shedler, Jonathan. "The Efficacy of Psychodynamic Psychotherapy." *American Psychologist*. February–March 2010. http://www.apa.org/pubs/ journals/releases/amp-65-2-98.pdf. Accessed 2/20/21.

Shields, Brooke. "War of Words." *The New York Times*. 1 July 2005. http:// www.nytimes.com/2005/07/01/opinion/war-of-words.html. Accessed 2/20/21.

Serpell, James. "Animal Companions and Human Well-Being: An Historical Exploration of the Value of Human-Animal Relationships." *Handbook on Animal-Assisted Therapy: Theoretical Foundations and Guidelines for Practice*. Cambridge, Massachusetts: Academic Press, 2000.

"Smartphone Addiction Facts and Statistics." Bagby.com. https://bagby. co/blogs/digital-wellbeing-pills/smartphone-addiction-facts-statistics-updated-2020. Accessed 2/20/21.

Smith, Jen Rose. "Before Coronavirus We Were Dying of Loneliness. Can a Pandemic Help America Heal?" CNN.com. 17 April 2020. https://www. cnn.com/2020/04/17/health/loneliness-epidemic-coronavirus-healing-wellness/index.html. Accessed 2/5/21.

Smith, Kathleen. "Substance Abuse and Depression." Psycom.net. https:// www.psycom.net/depression-substance-abuse. Accessed 3/12/21.

Smits, Fransje, and Tim Huijts. "Treatment for Depression in 63 Countries Worldwide: Describing and Explaining Cross-National Differences." University of Luxembourg and University of London. *Health*

& *Place Journal*, vol. 31. January 2015. DOI: https://doi.org/10.1016/j. healthplace.2014.10.002. Abstract on Science Direct.com: https://www. sciencedirect.com/science/article/abs/pii/S1353829214001488. Accessed 3/30/21.

Solovitch, Sara. "Onetime Party Drug Hailed as Miracle for Treating Severe Depression." *The Washington Post*. 1 February 2016. https://www. washingtonpost.com/national/health-science/a-one-time-party-drug-is-helping-people-with-deep-depression/2016/02/01/d3e73862-b490-11e5-a76a-0b5145e8679a_story.html. Accessed 2/20/21.

Stone, Karli. "8 Facts About Depression and Mental Health in South Asia." The Borgen Project. 8 December 2020. https://borgenproject.org/ depression-and-mental-health-in-south-asia/. Accessed 3/20/21.

Stratton, Andrew. "Personal Trainer—History of This Practice." EzineArticles.com. 30 April 2010. http://ezinearticles.com/?Personal-Trainer---History-of-This-Practice&id=4206058. Accessed 2/20/21.

Svoboda, Elizabeth. "Gut Bacteria's Role in Anxiety and Depression: It's Not Just in Your Head." *Discover Magazine*. 4 October 2020. https:// www.discovermagazine.com/mind/gut-bacterias-role-in-anxiety-and-depression-its-not-just-in-your-head. Accessed 2/27/21.

"Technology and Mental Health." GeneSight.com blog. https://genesight. com/blog/patient/depression-and-technology-a-double-edged-sword/. Accessed 2/6/21.

Torborg, Liza, and Jennifer Vande Voort, M.D. "Mayo Clinic Q and A: New Treatment for Hard-to-Treat Depression." Mayo Clinic.org. 12 July 2019. https://newsnetwork.mayoclinic.org/discussion/mayo-clinic-q-and-a-new-treatment-for-hard-to-treat-depression. Accessed 2/26/21.

Vieta, Eduard, and Daniel Souery. "The Stark Reality of Living with

Depression in Europe." *Politico*. 29 June 2020. https://www.politico. eu/sponsored-content/the-stark-reality-of-living-with-depression-in-europe/. Accessed 3/20/21.

Wakefield, Jane. "Is Social Media Causing Childhood Depression?" BBC. com. 18 February 2020. https://bbc.com/news/technology-42705881. Accessed 2/13/21.

"What are the Treatments for Depression?" Health.gov.au. https://www1. health.gov.au/internet/publications/publishing.nsf/Content/mental-pubs-c-coping-toc~mental-pubs-c-coping-wha. Accessed 3/20/21.

"What is Internet Addiction?" HealthyPlace.com. 21 November 2016. https://www.healthyplace.com/addictions/center-for-internet-addiction-recovery/what-is-internet-addiction. Accessed 2/13/21.

"What is Neurofeedback?" International Society for Neurofeedback & Research pamphlet. 16553-Article-Text-64896-1-10-20160826.pdf. Accessed 2/20/21.

"What Is Psychopharmacology?" American Society of Clinical Psychopharmacology. ASCPP.org. http://www.ascpp.org/resources/information-for-patients/what-is-psychopharmacology. Accessed 2/22/21.

Willsher, Kim; Philip Oltermann, Vittorio Infante, & Paul Hamilos. "How Depression Treatment Differs throughout Europe." *The Guardian*. 21 November 2013. https://www.theguardian.com/society/2013/nov/21/depression-treatment-antidepressants-europe. Accessed 3/20/21.

"Winston Churchill and His 'Black Dog' that Helped Win World War II." National Alliance on Mental Illness.

"Young Adult Depression." Child Trends/DataBank Indicator. 2018.

https://www.childtrends.org/indicators/young-adult-depression. Accessed 2/20/21.

Young, Joel, M.D. "The Effects of 'Helicopter Parenting': How You Might be Increasing Your Child's Anxiety." PsychologyToday.com. 25 January 2017.

Young, K. and Rodgers, R. (1998). The Relationship Between Depression and Internet Addiction. *CyberPsychology & Behavior.* 1(1), 25-28. https://www.healthyplace.com/addictions/center-for-internet-addiction-recovery/relationship-between-depression-and-internet-addiction. Accessed 2/22/21.

Ypsilanti, A.; L. Lazuras, P. Powell, & P. Overton. (2018). "Self-Disgust as a Potential Mechanism Explaining the Association Between Loneliness and Depression." *The Journal of Affective Disorders.* DOI: 10.1016/j.jad.2018.09.056. Accessed 2/20/21.

**Books**
Andrews, Linda Wasmer. *Encyclopedia of Depression.* Santa Barbara, California: Greenwood, 2010.

Arkham, J.C., Christopher J. Garcia, and Chuck Serface. *Claims Department: Robin Williams Memorial: Comedian, Actor, Legend.* Lernersville, North Carolina: Office Supply Publishing, 2014.

Burgess, Wes. *The Depression Answer Book: Professional Answers to More than 275 Critical Questions about Medication, Therapy, Support & More.* Naperville, Illinois: Sourcebooks, Inc., 2009.

Clak, David A., and Aaron T. Beck, MD. *Scientific Foundations of Cognitive Theory and Therapy of Depression.* Hoboken, New Jersey: John Wiley & Sons, Inc., 1999.

Dukakis, Kitty, and Larry Lye. *Shock: The Healing Power of Electroconvulsive Therapy*. London, England: Penguin Group (USA), Inc., 2006.

Ehrenberg, Alain. *The Weariness of the Self: Diagnosing the History of Depression in the Contemporary Age*. Montreal, Quebec: McGill Queens University Press, 2010.

Emmons, Henry, MD. *The Chemistry of Joy: A Three-Step Program for Overcoming Depression through Western Science and Eastern Wisdom*. New York, New York: Simon & Schuster, 2006.

Engel, Jonathan. *American Therapy: The Rise of Psychotherapy in the United States*. London, England: Gotham Books, 2008.

Hirshbein, Laura D. *American Melancholy: Constructions of Depression in the Twentieth Century*. New Brunswick, New Jersey: Rutgers University Press, 2009.

Ilardi, Stephen S., Ph.D. *The Depression Cure: The 6-Step Program to Beat Depression without Drugs*. Cambridge, Massachusetts: Da Capo Press, 2009.

Irons, Chris. *Depression*. Basingstoke, England: Palgrave Macmillan, 2014.

Lawlor, Clark. *From Melancholia to Prozac: A History of Depression*. Bethesda, Maryland: Oxford University Press, 2012.

Marchand, William R., M.D. *Depression and Bipolar Disorder: Your Guide to Recovery*. Boulder, Colorado: Bull Publishing Company, 2012.

Phelps, Jim, M.D. *Why Am I Still Depressed?: Recognizing and Managing the Ups and Downs of Bipolar II and Soft Bipolar Disorder*. New York, New York: McGraw-Hill, 2006.

Rideout, V., & M.B. Robb. *The Common Sense Census: Media Use by Kids Age Zero to Eight, 2020*. San Francisco, California: Common Sense Media, 2020. https://www.commonsensemedia.org/sites/default/files/uploads/research/2020_zero_to_eight_census_final_web.pdf. Accessed 2/13/21.

Sharpe, Katherine. *Coming of Age on Zoloft: How Antidepressants Cheered Us Up, Let Us Down, and Changed Who We Are*. New York, New York: Harper Perennial, 2012.

Walker, Carl. *Depression and Globalization: The Politics of Mental Health in the 21st Century*. Berlin, Germany: Springer Science & Business Media, 2007.

Wehrenberg, Margaret. *The 10 Best-Ever Depression Management Techniques: Understanding How Your Brain Makes You Depressed & What You Can Do to Change It*. New York, New York: W.W. Norton & Company, 2010.

Weintraub, Amy. *Yoga for Depression: A Compassionate Guide to Relieve Suffering through Yoga*. New York, New York: Broadway Books, 2004.

Wright, Jesse H., and Laura W. McCray. *Breaking Free from Depression: Pathways to Wellness*. New York, New York: Guilford Publications, Inc., 2012.

Zetin, Mark, Cara T. Hoepner, and Jennifer Kurth. *Challenging Depression: The Go-To Guide for Clinicians and Patients*. New York, New York: W.W. Norton & Company, Inc., 2010.

**Interviews**
Baumann, Heidi. Phone interview by Sarah Hamaker. Tape recording. 14 July 2015.

Bruno, Bryan. Email interview by Sarah Hamaker. 22 January 2021.

Clancy, Liza R. Email interview by Sarah Hamaker. 25 January 2021.

Cozzolino, Callandre. Phone interview by Sarah Hamaker. Tape recording. 25 August 2015.

Irwin, Nancy. Email interview by Sarah Hamaker. 24 January 2021.

Lee, Crystal I. Phone interview by Sarah Hamaker. 11 September 2017.

Litzsinger, Dick. Phone interview by Sarah Hamaker. Tape recording. 1 July 2015.

Litzsinger, Dona. Phone Interview by Sarah Hamaker. Tape recording. 9 December 2015.

Litzsinger, Robin. Phone interview by Sarah Hamaker. Tape recording. 9 July 2015.

Litzsinger, Todd. Phone interview by Sarah Hamaker. Tape recording. 17 July 2015.

Manning, Virginia. Phone interview by Sarah Hamaker. 26 February 2021.

Norman, Suzanne. Phone interview by Sarah Hamaker. 15 September 2017.

Norouzi, Arayeh. Email interview by Sarah Hamaker. 30 January 2021.

Pollack, Mark. Phone interview by Sarah Hamaker. Tape recording. 26 August 2015.

Reimer, Deborahanne. Phone interview by Sarah Hamaker. 11 September 2017.

Rivera, Zak. Phone interview by Sarah Hamaker. Tape recording. 28 August 2015.

Scheftner, William. Phone interview by Sarah Hamaker. Tape recording. 22 September 2015.

Senner, Bonnie. Phone interview by Sarah Hamaker. Tape recording. 5 August 2015.

Shulman, Robert. Phone interview by Sarah Hamaker. 1 February 2021.

Stratman, Shawn. Phone interview by Sarah Hamaker. Tape recording. 2 July 2015.

Zakeri, Lynn R. Phone interview by Sarah Hamaker. 8 September 2017 and 27 January 2021.

# ENDNOTES

**Introduction**

[1] Scheftner, William. Phone interview by Sarah Hamaker. Tape recording. 22 September 2015.

**Chapter 1**

[2] Lawlor, Clark. From Melancholia to Prozac: A History of Depression. Bethesda, Maryland: Oxford University Press, 2012. 2.

[3] Jansson, Asa. "Mood Disorders and the Brain: Depression, Melancholia, and the Historiography of Psychiatry." Cambridge University Press and U.S. National Library of Medicine, National Institutes of Health, July 2011. www.ncbi.nlm.nih.gov/pmc/articles/PMC3143872/. Accessed 2/18/21. 2.

[4] Lawlor, 5.

[5] Ehrenberg, Alain. The Weariness of the Self: Diagnosing the History of Depression in the Contemporary Age. Montreal, Quebec: McGill Queens University Press, 2010. 7 (preface).

[6] Ibid, 24–25 (preface).

[7] Jansson, 1.

[8] Neergaard, Lauran. "Task Force Urges Doctors to Screen All Adults for Depression." Associated Press/The Washington Post. 26 January 2016. https://www.washingtonpost.com/national/health-science/task-force-urges-doctors-to-screen-all-adults-for-depression/2016/01/26/9fb49fba-c44b-11e5-b933-31c93021392a_story.html. Accessed 2/3/2016.

[9] "Depression." World Health Organization. 30 January 2020. https://www.who.

int/news-room/fact-sheets/detail/depression. Accessed 3/30/21.

[10] Ibid.

[11] Levine, David. "A Look at Depression Around the World." *U.S. News and World Report*. 7 July 2017. https://health.usnews.com/health-care/patient-advice/articles/2017-07-07/a-look-at-depression-around-the-world. Accessed 3/30/21.

**Chapter 2**

[12] Ibid.

[13] Ibid.

[14] Dewey, Caitlin. "A Stunning Map of Depression Rates around the World." *The Washington Post*. 7 November 2013. https://www.washingtonpost.com/news/worldviews/wp/2013/11/07/a-stunning-map-of-depression-rates-around-the-world/. Accessed 3/30/21.

[15] Shulman, Robert. Phone interview by Sarah Hamaker. 1 February 2021.

[16] Smits, Fransje and Huijts, Tim. "Treatment for Depression in 63 Countries Worldwide: Describing and Explaining Cross-National Differences." University of Luxembourg and University of London. Published in *Health & Place Journal*, Vol. 31. January 2015. DOI: https://doi.org/10.1016/j.healthplace.2014.10.002. Abstract on Science Direct.com: https://www.sciencedirect.com/science/article/abs/pii/S1353829214001488. Accessed 3/30/21.

[17] Pogosyan, Marianna. "How Culture Affects Depression." *Psychology Today*. 6 December 2017. https://www.psychologytoday.com/us/blog/between-cultures/201712/how-culture-affects-depression. Accessed 3/30/21.

[18] Ibid.

[19] Ibid.

[20] Ibid.

[21] "Depression in Europe: Facts and Figures." World Health Organization. https://www.euro.who.int/en/health-topics/noncommunicable-diseases/mental-health/news/news/2012/10/depression-in-europe/depression-in-europe-facts-and-figures. Accessed 3/20/21.

[22] Willsher, Kim, Philip Oltermann, Vittorio Infante, and Paul Hamilos. "How Depression Treatment Differs throughout Europe." *The Guardian*. 21 November 2013. https://www.theguardian.com/society/2013/nov/21/depression-treatment-antidepressants-europe. Accessed 3/20/21.

[23] Ibid.

[24] Ibid.

[25] Ibid.

[26] Vieta, Eduard, and Daniel Souery. "The Stark Reality of Living with Depression in Europe." *Politico*. 29 June 2020. https://www.politico.eu/sponsored-content/the-stark-reality-of-living-with-depression-in-europe. Accessed 3/20/21.

[27] Ibid.

[28] Ibid.

[29] Ibid.

[30] Ibid.

[31] Ibid.

[32] Ibid.

[33] Stone, Karli. "8 Facts About Depression and Mental Health in South Asia." The Borgen Project. 8 December 2020. https://borgenproject.org/depression-and-mental-health-in-south-asia. Accessed 3/20/21.

[34] Ibid.

[35] Ibid.

[36] Chee KY, et al. "Country Variations in Depressive Symptoms Profile in Asian Countries: Findings of the Research on Asia Psychotropic Prescription (REAP) Studies." *Asia-Pacific Psychiatry*. 2015 Sep; 7(3):276-85. doi: 10.1111/appy.12170. Epub 13 January 2015. PMID: 25641910. https://pubmed.ncbi.nlm.nih.gov/25641910. Accessed 3/20/21.

[37] "The Facts." Beyond Blue.org. https://www.beyondblue.org.au/the-facts. Accessed 3/20/21.

[38] "Depression." Sane.org. 21 May 2001. https://www.sane.org/information-stories/facts-and-guides/depression. Accessed 3/20/21.

[39] "What are the Treatments for Depression?" Health.gov.au. https://www1.health.gov.au/internet/publications/publishing.nsf/Content/mental-pubs-c-coping-toc~mental-pubs-c-coping-wha. Accessed 3/20/21.

[40] Ibid.

[41] "Depression." Sane.org.

[42] "Poor Mental Health, An Obstacle to Development in Latin America." World Bank.org. 13 July 2015. https://www.worldbank.org/en/news/feature/2015/07/13/bad-mental-health-obstacle-development-latin-america. Accessed 3/20/21.

[43] Bocanegra, Juan. "Mental Health: A Problem We Need to Take Care of in Latin America." *Latin American Post*. 6 April 2019. https://latinamericanpost. com/27444-mental-health-a-problem-we-need-to-take-care-of-in-latin-america. Accessed 3/20/21.

[44] "Depression." Pan American Health Organization. https://www.paho.org/en/ topics/depression. Accessed 3/20/21.

[45] "Poor Mental Health, An Obstacle to Development in Latin America."

[46] Ibid.

[47] Ibid.

[48] Huizen, Jennifer. "What to Know about Mental Health Stigma in Latin America." *Medical News Today*. 27 January 2021. https://www.medicalnewstoday. com/articles/mental-health-stigma-in-latin-america. Accessed 3/20/21.

[49] Ibid.

[50] Ibid.

[51] "Poor Mental Health, An Obstacle to Development in Latin America."

[52] Mayton, Rosie, et al. "Explanatory models of depression in sub-Saharan Africa: Synthesis of qualitative evidence." *Social Science & Medicine*. Vol. 246. February 2020. DOI: 10.1016j.socscimed.2019.112760, https://www.sciencedirect.com/ science/article/pii/S0277953619307555. Accessed 3/20/21.

[53] Sankoh, Osman, Stephen Sevalie, and Mark Weston. "Mental Health in Africa." *The Lancet*, Vol. 6, issue 9, E954-E955. 1 September 2018. DOI: 10.1016/S2214-109X(18)30303-6, https://www.thelancet.com/journals/langlo/article/PIIS2214-109X(18)30303-6/fulltext. Accessed 3/20/21.

[54] Mayton.

[55] Gberie, Lansana. "Mental Illness: Invisible but Devastating." *Africa Renewal*. December 2016-March 2017. https://www.un.org/africarenewal/magazine/ december-2016-march-2017/mental-illness-invisible-devastating. Accessed 3/20/21.

[56] Ibid.

[57] Ibid.

[58] Ibid.

[59] Ibid.

[60] Ibid.

[61] Ibid.

[62] Sankoh.

[63] Ibid.

**Chapter 3**

[64] Walker, Carl. *Depression and Globalization: The Politics of Mental Health in the 21st Century.* Berlin, Germany: Springer Science & Business Media, 2007. 45.

[65] Andrews, Linda Wasmer. *Encyclopedia of Depression.* Santa Barbara, California: Greenwood, 2010. 473.

[66] Walker, 47.

[67] Ibid.

[68] Irons, Chris. *Depression.* Basingstoke, England: Palgrave Macmillan, 2014. 183.

[69] Borresen, Kelsey. "Artist Channels How Depression Feels Into Beautiful Drawings." Healthy Living section of the *Huffington Post.* 11 August 2017. http://www.huffingtonpost.com/entry/artist-depression-illustrations_us_598cd864e4b090964295eef3?ncid=APPLENEWS00001. Accessed 2/10/21. 1.

[70] Andrews, 473.

[71] Walker, 47–48.

[72] Stratman, Shawn. Phone interview by Sarah Hamaker. Tape recording. 2 July 2015.

[73] Andrews, 473.

[74] Walker, 46.

[75] Andrews, 473.

[76] "Winston Churchill and His 'Black Dog' that Helped Win World War II." National Alliance on Mental Illness.

[77] Ibid.

[78] Litzsinger, Dick. Phone interview by Sarah Hamaker. Tape recording. 1 July 2015.

[79] Shields, Brooke. "War of Words." *The New York Times.* 1 July 2005. http://www.nytimes.com/2005/07/01/opinion/war-of-words.html?_r=0. Accessed 2/20/21. 1.

[80] Ibid.

[81] Fontana, Francesca. "Some Companies Want You to Take a Mental-Health Day." *The Wall Street Journal.* 15 August 2017. https://www.wsj.com/articles/why-some-companies-want-you-to-take-a-mental-health-day-1502789400. Accessed

2/16/21.

[82] Shields.

[83] Rothkopf, Joanna. "Autopsy: Robin Williams Had Lewy Body Dementia." Salon.com. 13 November 2014. http://www.salon.com/2014/11/13/autopsy_robin_williams_had_lewy_body_dementia/. Accessed 2/20/21.

[84] Ruiz, Rebecca. "Finally, We're Talking about Mental Illness Like Adults." Mashable.com. 13 August 2014. http://mashable.com/2014/08/13/robin-williams-mental-health-stigma/#yg3qCXjFa8qW. Accessed 2/20/21. 1.

[85] Arkham, J.C., Christopher J. Garcia, and Chuck Serface. *Claims Department: Robin Williams Memorial: Comedian, Actor, Legend.* Lernersville, North Carolina: Office Supply Publishing, 2014. 37.

[86] Andrews, 473.

[87] List compiled from http://www.wcvb.com/health/14414700 and https://en.wikipedia.org/wiki/List_of_people_with_major_depressive_disorder. Accessed 10/30/15.

[88] Reimer, Deborahanne. Phone interview by Sarah Hamaker. 11 September 2017.


**Chapter 4**

[89] "Depression in Children and Teens." *American Academy of Child & Adolescent Psychiatry.* No. 4; Updated October 2018. http://www.aacap.org/AACAP/Families_and_Youth/Facts_for_Families/FFF-Guide/The-Depressed-Child-004.aspx. Accessed 2/10/21.

[90] Dryden-Edwards, Roxanne, MD. "Teen Depression: 10 Warning Signs for Teen Suicide." MedicineNet.com. http://www.medicinenet.com/teen_depression/article.htm. Accessed 2/16/21.

[91] Ibid.

[92] Lee, Crystal I. Phone interview by Sarah Hamaker. 11 September 2017.

[93] "Major Depression among Adolescents." National Institute of Mental Health Staff. National Institute of Mental Health, National Institutes of Health. https://www.nimh.nih.gov/health/statistics/prevalence/major-depression-among-adolescents.shtml. Accessed 8/19/17.

[94] Ibid.

[95] Cha, Ariana Eunjung. "More than a Third of Teenage Girls Experience Depression, New Study Says." *The Washington Post.* 31 May 2017. https://

www.washingtonpost.com/news/to-your-health/wp/2017/05/31/more-than-a-third-of-teenage-girls-experience-depression-new-study-says/?utm_term=. c4a7dd6223ca. Accessed 2/10/21.

[96] Zakeri, Lynn R. Phone interview by Sarah Hamaker. 8 September 2017 and 27 January 2021.

[97] Nierenberg, Cari. "7 Ways to Recognize Depression in 20-Somethings." Live Science.com. 27 October 2016. https://www.livescience.com/56602-signs-depression-young-adults.html. Accessed 2/16/21.

[98] "Young Adult Depression." Child Trends/DataBank Indicator. https://www. childtrends.org/indicators/young-adult-depression. Accessed 2/20/21.

[99] Ibid.

[100] Ibid.

[101] Nierenberg.

[102] "Young Adult Depression."

[103] Nauert, Rick, Ph.D. "Long-Term Use of Opioids Ups Risk for Depression." PsychCentral.com. 13 January 2016. https://psychcentral.com/news/2016/01/13/long-term-use-of-opioids-up-risk-for-depression/97577.html. Accessed 9/2/17.

[104] Ibid.

[105] Ibid.

[106] Dryden-Edwards.

[107] Kelly, Kate. "How Loneliness Can Impact Kids With Learning and Attention Issues." Understood.org. https://www.understood.org/en/friends-feelings/managing-feelings/loneliness-sadness-isolation/how-loneliness-can-impact-kids-with-learning-and-attention-issues. Accessed 9/20/17.

[108] Lalayants, Marina, and Jonathan D. Prince. "Loneliness and Depression or Depression-Related Factors among Child Welfare-Involved Adolescent Females." *Child and Adolescent Social Work Journal.* April 2015, Volume 32, Issue 2. https://link.springer.com/article/10.1007/s10560-014-0344-6. Accessed 2/18/21.

[109] "Lack of Parental Support during Childhood Is Associated with Increased Adult Depression and Chronic Health Problems, Study Finds." American Psychological Association. 21 March 2004. http://www.apa.org/news/press/releases/2004/03/parental-support.aspx. Accessed 2/18/21.

[110] Lalayants.

[111] Bergland, Christopher. "Parental Warmth Is Crucial for a Child's Well-Being:

Toxic Childhood Stress Alters Neural Responses Linked to Illness in Adulthood." PsychologyToday.com. 4 October 2013. https://www.psychologytoday.com/ blog/the-athletes-way/201310/parental-warmth-is-crucial-child-s-well-being. Accessed 2/10/21.

[112] Ibid.

[113] Young, Joel, M.D. "The Effects of 'Helicopter Parenting': How You Might Be Increasing Your Child's Anxiety." PsychologyToday.com. 25 January 2017. https://www.psychologytoday.com/blog/when-your-adult-child-breaks-your-heart/201701/the-effects-helicopter-parenting. Accessed 2/18/21.

[114] Asa, Richard. "Dangers of Helicopter Parenting When Your Kids Are Teens." ChicagoTribune.com. 23 June 2015. http://www.chicagotribune.com/lifestyles/ sc-fam-0630-teen-helicopter-parent-20150623-story.html. Accessed 2/10/21.

[115] Schiffrin, Holly H., Miriam Liss, Haley Miles-McLean, Katherine A. Geary, Mindy J. Erchull, and Taryn Tashner "Helping or Hovering? The Effects of Helicopter Parenting on College Students' Well-Being." *Journal of Child and Family Studies*. April 2014, Volume 23, Issue 3, 548–557. https://link.springer. com/article/10.1007/s10826-013-9716-3. Accessed 2/20/21.

[116] Ibid.

[117] Lythcott-Haims, Julie. "Kids of Helicopter Parents Are Sputtering Out." *How to Raise an Adult: Break Free of the Overparenting Trap and Prepare Your Kid for Success*, excerpt on Slate.com. 5 July 2015. http://www.slate.com/articles/ double_x/doublex/2015/07/helicopter_parenting_is_increasingly_correlated_ with_college_age_depression.html. Accessed 2/18/21.

[118] Asa.

[119] Goldberg, Emma. "Teens in Covid Isolation: 'I Felt Like I Was Suffocating.'" *The New York Times*. 12 November 2020. https://www.nytimes.com/2020/11/12/ health/covid-teenagers-mental-health.html. Accessed 2/2/21.

[120] McClurg, Lesley. "Pandemic Takes Toll on Children's Mental Health." NPR. org. 28 November 2020. https://www.npr.org/2020/11/28/938460892/pandemic-takes-toll-on-childrens-mental-health. Accessed 2/2/21.

[121] Miranda, D., Athanasio, B., Oliveira, A., Simeos-e-Silva, A. "How is the COVID-19 Pandemic Impacting Mental Health of Children and Adolescents?" NIH.gov. 10 September 2020. DOI: 10.1016/j.ijdrr.2020.101845.

[122] McClurg.

[123] Ibid.

[124] Ibid.

[125] Ibid.

[126] Scott, Larissa. "Doctors Worry as Mental Health Issues with Children Increase During Pandemic". ABC Action News. 29 December 2020. https://www.abcactionnews.com/rebound/coronavirus-stress/doctors-worry-as-mental-health-issues-with-children-increase-during-pandemic. Accessed 2/2/21.

[127] Hadler, Nicole. "Coping with the COVID-19 Pandemic as a College Student." University of Michigan.edu. https://medicine.umich.edu/dept/psychiatry/michigan-psychiatry-resources-covid-19/adults-specific-resources/coping-covid-19-pandemic-college-student. Accessed 2/2/21.

[128] John, Arit. "Increased Anxiety and Depression Top College Students' Concerns in Coronavirus Survey." 25 March 2020. *The Los Angeles Times*. https://www.latimes.com/california/story/2020-03-25/college-students-anxiety-depression-coronavirus-survey. Accessed 2/2/21.

[129] Ibid.

[130] Dennon, Anne. "Coronavirus Impacts on Students and Online Learning." 15 December 2020, BestColleges.com. https://www.bestcolleges.com/blog/coronavirus-impacts-on-students. Accessed 2/2/21.

[131] Hadler.

[132] John.

[133] Dryden-Edwards.

[134] "Depression in Children and Teens."

[135] "Helping Young Adult Children Cope with Depression." MentalHealthTreatment.net. http://mentalhealthtreatment.net/helping-young-adult-children-cope-with-depression. Accessed 2/18/21.

[136] Dryden-Edwards.

[137] "Mental Health During COVID-19: Signs Your Child May Need More Support." Healthy Children.org. 23 October 2021. https://www.healthychildren.org/English/health-issues/conditions/COVID-19/Pages/Signs-your-Teen-May-Need-More-Support.aspx. Accessed 2/2/21.

[138] Ibid.

[139] Ibid.

[140] Scott.

[141] McClurg.

[142] "Depression in Children and Teens."

[143] "Antidepressants for Children and Teens." Mayo Clinic Staff, MayoClinic. org. http://www.mayoclinic.org/diseases-conditions/teen-depression/in-depth/antidepressants/ART-20047502. Accessed 2/10/21.

[144] Ibid.

[145] Ibid.

[146] Ibid.

[147] Cha.

[148] "Depression in Children and Teens."

[149] Dryden-Edwards.

[150] "Young Adult Depression."

[151] "Depression in Children and Teens."

[152] Dryden-Edwards.

[153] Hadler.

[154] Ibid.

[155] Ibid.

**Chapter 5**

[156] Petroff, Alanna. "Google is Offering a Test for Depression." CNN. 24 August 2017. http://money.cnn.com/2017/08/24/technology/google-depression-questionnaire/index.html. Accessed 2/16/21. 1.

[157] Ibid.

**Chapter 6**

[158] Litzsinger, Dona. Phone Interview by Sarah Hamaker. Tape recording. 9 December 2015.

[159] Litzsinger, Robin. Phone interview by Sarah Hamaker. Tape recording. 9 July 2015.

[160] Baumann, Heidi. Phone interview by Sarah Hamaker. Tape recording. 14 July 2015.

[161] Stratman, Shawn. Phone interview by Sarah Hamaker. Tape recording. 2 July 2015.

[162] Litzsinger, Todd. Phone interview by Sarah Hamaker. Tape recording. 17 July

2015.

[163] Pollack, Mark. Phone interview by Sarah Hamaker. Tape recording. 26 August 2015.

[164] Clancy, Liza R. Email interview by Sarah Hamaker. 25 January 2021.

**Chapter 7**

[165] "Managing Loneliness During COVID-19." Sharp Mesa Vista Hospital. 8 September 2020. https://www.sharp.com/health-news/managing-loneliness-during-covid-19.cfm. Accessed 2/5/21.

[166] Cherry, Kendra. "The Health Consequences of Loneliness: Causes and Health Consequences of Feeling Lonely." Verywellmind.com. 23 March 2020. https://www.verywellmind.com/loneliness-causes-effects-and-treatments-2795749. Accessed 2/5/21.

[167] Raypole, Crystal. "Loneliness and Depression: What's the Connection?" Healthline.com. 2 July 2020. https://www.healthline.com/health/loneliness-and-depression. Accessed 2/5/21.

[168] Ibid.

[169] Bruno, Dr. Bryan. Email interview by Sarah Hamaker. 22 January 2021.

[170] Ypsilanti, A., Lazuras, L., Powell, P., Overton, P. (2018). "Self-Disgust as a Potential Mechanism Explaining the Association Between Loneliness and Depression." *The Journal of Affective Disorders.* DOI: 10.1016/j.jad.2018.09.056.

[171] Raypole.

[172] Ducharme, Jamie. "COVID-19 is Making America's Loneliness Epidemic Even Worse." Time.com. 8 May 2020. https://time.com/5833681/loneliness-covid-19. Accessed 2/5/21.

[173] Smith, Jen Rose. "Before Coronavirus We Were Dying of Loneliness. Can a Pandemic Help America Heal?" CNN.com. 17 April 2020. https://www.cnn.com/2020/04/17/health/loneliness-epidemic-coronavirus-healing-wellness/index.html. Accessed 2/5/21.

[174] Ibid.

[175] Pinker, Susan. "The Science of Staying Connected." *The Wall Street Journal.* 2 April 2020. https://www.wsj.com/articles/the-science-of-staying-connected-11585835999. Accessed 2/5/21.

[176] Ducharme.

[177] Ibid.

[178] Ibid.

[179] "COVID-19 Has Produced 'Alarming' Increase in Loneliness." Medical News Today.com. 25 November 2020. https://www.medicalnewstoday.com/articles/alarming-covid-19-study-shows-80-of-respondents-report-significant-symptoms-of-depression. Accessed 2/5/21.

[180] Jargon, Julie. "Lonely Girls: How the Pandemic Has Deepened the Isolation of Adolescents." *The Wall Street Journal.* 29 July 2020. https://www.wsj.com/articles/lonely-girls-how-the-pandemic-has-deepened-the-isolation-of-adolescents-11595937600. Accessed 2/5/21.

[181] Ducharme.

[182] Morris, Betsy. "Quarantining the Elderly is Harmful to their Health." The Wall Street Journal. 21 July 2020.

[183] Ducharme.

[184] Seppala, Emma. "Eight Ways to Ease the Pain of Loneliness." The Greater Good Science Center. 2 October 2020. https://greatergood.berkeley.edu/article/item/eight_ways_to_ease_the_pain_of_loneliness. Accessed 2/5/21.

[185] Smith.

[186] Petersen, Andrea. "The Struggle to Cope With Depression Amid Coronavirus." *The Wall Street Journal.* 12 April 2020. https://www.wsj.com/articles/the-struggle-to-cope-with-depression-amid-coronavirus-11586696401. Accessed 2/5/21.

[187] Raypole.

[188] Ibid.

[189] Seppala.

[190] "COVID-19 and Your Mental Health." MayoClinic.org. 15 October 2020. https://www.mayoclinic.org/diseases-conditions/coronavirus/in-depth/mental-health-covid-19/art-20482731. Accessed 2/5/21.

[191] Seppala.

[192] Ibid.

[193] "COVID-19 and Your Mental Health."

[194] Ibid.

[195] Ibid.

[196] Seppala.

[197] Ibid.

[198] "COVID-19 and Your Mental Health."

## Chapter 8

[199] Norouzi, Arayeh. Email interview by Sarah Hamaker. 30 January 2021.

[200] Alavi, S. S., Maracy, M. R., Jannatifard, F., & Eslami, M. (2011). The effect of psychiatric symptoms on the internet addiction disorder in Isfahan's University students. *Journal of Research in Medical Sciences: The Official Journal of Isfahan University of Medical Sciences*, 16(6), 793–800. https://www.ncbi.nlm.nih.gov/pmc/articles/PMC3214398/#:~:text=Excessive%20Internet%20use%20may%20create,low%20family%20relationships%20and%20anxiety. Accessed 2/22/21.

[201] Ibid.

[202] Young, K. and Rodgers, R. (1998). "The Relationship Between Depression and Internet Addiction." *CyberPsychology & Behavior*. 1(1), 25-28. https://www.healthyplace.com/addictions/center-for-internet-addiction-recovery/relationship-between-depression-and-internet-addiction. Accessed 2/22/21.

[203] Ibid.

[204] "What is Internet Addiction?" HealthyPlace.com. 21 November 2016. https://www.healthyplace.com/addictions/center-for-internet-addiction-recovery/what-is-internet-addiction. Accessed 2/13/21.

[205] Alexander, Donovan, "Technology Addiction: When is Technology Too Much?" 16 August 2020. https://interestingengineering.com/technology-addiction-when-is-technology-too-much. Accessed 2/13/21.

[206] Ibid.

[207] Miller, Caroline. "Is Internet Addiction Real?" Child Mind.org, accessed February 13, 2021. https://childmind.org/article/is-internet-addiction-real. Accessed 2/13/21.

[208] Ibid.

[209] Rideout, V., & Robb, M. B. *The Common Sense Census: Media Use by Kids Age Zero to Eight, 2020*. San Francisco, California: Common Sense Media, 2020. https://www.commonsensemedia.org/sites/default/files/uploads/research/2020_zero_to_eight_census_final_web.pdf. Accessed 2/13/21.

[210] Ibid.

[211] Ibid.

[212] Wakefield, Jane. "Is Social Media Causing Childhood Depression?" BBC.

com. 18 February 2020. https://bbc.com/news/technology-42705881. Accessed 2/13/21.

213 Ibid.

214 Reinberg, Steven. "Addictive Internet Use Tied to Depression in Teens." HealthDay News on Medicine Net.com. 2 August 2020. https://www.medicinenet.com/script/main/art.asp?articlekey=118570. Accessed 2/22/21.

215 Ibid.

216 Ibid.

217 Garcia-Navarro, Lulu. "The Risk of Teen Depression and Suicide is Linked to Smartphone Use, Study Says." NPR.org. 17 December 2017. https://www.npr.org/2017/12/17/571443683/the-call-in-teens-and-depression. Accessed 2/22/21.

218 Ibid.

219 Ibid.

220 "Technology and Mental Health." GeneSight.com blog. https://genesight.com/blog/patient/depression-and-technology-a-double-edged-sword/. Accessed 2/6/21.

221 Odgers, C. & Robb, M. B. *Tweens, Teens, Tech, and Mental Health: Coming of Age in an Increasingly Digital, Uncertain, and Unequal World, 2020*. San Francisco, California: Common Sense Media, 2020. https://www.commonsensemedia.org/sites/default/files/uploads/pdfs/tweens-teens-tech-and-mental-health-full-report-final-for-web1.pdf. Accessed 2/13/21.

222 Ibid.

223 Newport, Frank. "Most U.S. Smartphone Owners Check Phone at Least Hourly." Gallup.com. 9 July 2015. https://news.gallup.com/poll/184046/smartphone-owners-check-phone-least-hourly.aspx. Accessed 2/13/21.

224 Banducci, Sarah. "Mobile Device Addiction Linked to Depression, Anxiety." Science Daily.com. 2 March 2016. https://www.sciencedaily.com/releases/2016/03/160302121325.htm. Accessed 2/13/21.

225 Ibid.

226 Ibid.

227 Ibid.

228 Newport.

229 "Smartphone Addiction Facts and Statistics." Bagby.com. https://bagby.co/blogs/digital-wellbeing-pills/smartphone-addiction-facts-statistics-

updated-2020. Accessed 2/20/21.

[230] Glatter, Robert. "Digital Addiction: A Recipe for Isolation, Depression and Anxiety." Forbes.com. 30 April 2018. https://www.forbes.com/sites/robertglatter/2018/04/13/digital-addiction-a-recipe-for-isolation-depression-and-anxiety/?sh=364452bb5f6b. Accessed 2/20/21.

[231] "Smartphone Addiction Facts and Statistics."

[232] Ibid.

[233] Shulman, Robert. Phone interview by Sarah Hamaker. 1 February 2021.

**Chapter 9**

[234] Manning, Virginia Dale. Phone interview by Sarah Hamaker. 26 February 2021.

[235] Gordon, Sherri. "Why Mental Health Disorders Co-Exist with Substance Abuse." Verywellmind.com. 16 January 2021. https://www.verywellmind.com/co-occurring-disorders-mental-health-and-addiction-4158280. Accessed 3/5/21.

[236] Holland, Kimberly. "Understanding the Link Between Alcohol Use and Depression." Healthline.com. 25 June 2019. https://www.healthline.com/health/mental-health/alcohol-and-depression. Accessed 3/5/21.

[237] Irwin, Nancy. Email interview by Sarah Hamaker. 24 January 2021.

[238] Conner, Kenneth R et al. "Meta-analysis of depression and substance use among individuals with alcohol use disorders." *Journal of Substance Abuse Treatment*, Vol. 37, 2 (2009): 127-37. doi:10.1016/j.jsat.2008.11.007. https://www.ncbi.nlm.nih.gov/pmc/articles/PMC4864601. Accessed 3/5/21.

[239] "Depression and Addiction." DualDiagnosis.org. https://dualdiagnosis.org/depression-and-addiction. Accessed 3/5/21.

[240] Ibid.

[241] Gordon, Sherri.

[242] Ibid.

[243] Ibid.

[244] Smith, Kathleen. "Substance Abuse and Depression." Psycom.net. https://www.psycom.net/depression-substance-abuse. Accessed 3/12/21.

[245] Holland.

[246] Ibid.

247 Ibid.

248 Gordon, Sherri.

249 Conner.

250 Harrison, Rachel. "Drinking During COVID-19 Up Among People with Anxiety and Depression." New York University School of Global Public Health. 19 January 2021. https://www.nyu.edu/about/news-publications/news/2021/january/alcohol-use-covid-19.html. Accessed 3/5/21.

251 Ibid.

252 Ibid.

253 Holland.

254 Gordon, Sherri.

255 "Depression and Addiction."

256 Nelson, Jeff. "JoJo Reveals Clinical Depression Diagnosis: 'Sometimes We Just Need a Little Help.'" *People Magazine*. 29 April 2020. https://people.com/music/jojo-clinical-depression-family-addiction-struggles. Accessed 3/26/21.

257 Ibid.

258 Holland.

259 Smith, Kathleen.

260 Harrison.

261 Nolan, Lucas. "Elon Musk Claims His Brain Chip Will Cure Depression, Addiction." Breitbart.com. 13 July 2020. https://www.breitbart.com/tech/2020/07/13/elon-musk-claims-his-brain-chip-will-cure-depression-addiction. Accessed 3/5/21.

262 Ibid.

263 Ibid.

264 "Depression and Addiction."

**Chapter 10**

265 Burgess, Wes. *The Depression Answer Book*. Sourcebooks, Inc., 2009. 108.

266 Ibid, 109.

267 "Mental Health Providers: Tips on Finding One." MayoClinic.org. 18 February 2014. http://www.mayoclinic.org/diseases-conditions/mental-illness/in-depth/mental-health-providers/art-20045530. Accessed 2/18/21. 2.

268 "What Is Psychopharmacology." American Society of Clinical

Psychopharmacology. ASCPP.org. http://www.ascpp.org/resources/information-for-patients/what-is-psychopharmacology. Accessed 2/22/21. 1.

[269]Diamond, Stephen A., Ph.D. "The Psychology of Psychopharmacology." PsychologyToday.com. 18 April 2008. https://www.psychologytoday.com/blog/evil-deeds/200804/the-psychology-psychopharmacology. Accessed 2/10/21.

[270] "Burgess, 110.

[271] "Mental Health Providers: Tips on Finding One." 1.

[272] Burgess, 110.

[273] Ibid, 134.

[274] "Mental Health Providers: Tips on Finding One." 1.

[275] Burgess, 133.

## Chapter 12

[276] "Recognize the Warning Signs of Suicide." WebMD. September 2012. http://www.webmd.com/depression/guide/depression-recognizing-signs-of-suicide#3. Accessed 2/18/21. 1.

[277] Ibid.

## Chapter 13

[278] Hirshbein, Laura D. *American Melancholy: Constructions of Depression in the Twentieth Century.* New Brunswick, New Jersey: Rutgers University Press, 2009. 3.

[279] Ibid, 12.

[280] Miriam-Webster Online Medical Dictionary. http://www.merriam-webster.com/medical/allopathy. Accessed 1/18/16.

[281] Hirshbein., 12.

[282] Engel, Jonathan. *American Therapy: The Rise of Pyschotherapy in the United States.* London, England: Gotham Books, 2008. 9

[283] Ibid, 9.

[284] Ibid, 71.

[285] Ibid, 53.

[286] "Historical Understandings of Depression." MentalHelp.net. www.mentalhelp.net/articles/historical-understandings-of-depression. Accessed 2/18/21. 2.

[287] Ibid.

[288] Sharpe, Katherine. *Coming of Age on Zoloft: How Antidepressants Cheered Us Up, Let Us Down, and Changed Who We Are.* New York, New York: Harper Perennial, 2012. 35.

[289] Engel, 76.

[290] Sharpe, 38.

[291] Ibid, 39.

[292] Ibid.

[293] Clak, David A., and Aaron T. Beck, MD. *Scientific Foundations of Cognitive Theory and Therapy of Depression.* Hoboken, New Jersey: John Wiley & Sons, Inc., 1999. 37.

[294] Ibid, 39.

[295] Ibid, 39.

[296] Ibid, 39.

[297] Sharpe, 43.

[298] Ibid, 36.

[299] Engel, 242–243.

[300] Ibid.

[301] Ibid, 244.

[302] Ibid, 249.

[303] Ibid, 250.

[304] Ibid.

[305] Sharpe, 45.

[306] Ibid, 44.

[307] Engel, 251.

[308] Hirshbein, 75.

[309] Clak, 2.

**Chapter 14**

[310] Zetin, Mark, Cara T. Hoepner, and Jennifer Kurth. *Challenging Depression: The Go-To Guide for Clinicians and Patients.* New York, New York: W.W. Norton & Company, Inc., 2010. 26.

[311] Rao, Murali, MD, and Julie M. Alderson, DO. "New Depression Treatments Reported." ScienceDaily.com. February 2014. www.sciencedaily.com/releases/2014/02/140214130719.htm. Accessed 2/18/21.

[312] Wright, Jesse H., and Laura W. McCray. *Breaking Free from Depression: Pathways to Wellness.* New York, New York: Guilford Publications, Inc., 2012. 56.

[313] Ibid, 39.

[314] "Depression (Major Depressive Disorder)." MayoClinic.org. 3 February 2018. http://www.mayoclinic.org/diseases-conditions/depression/basics/definition/con-20032977. Accessed 2/10/21. 8.

[315] Zetin, 1.

[316] Ibid.

[317] Burgess, 25.

[318] Serani, Deborah, Psy.D. "Genetic Testing for Better Depression Treatment." *Psychology Today.* 1 July 2014. https://www.psychologytoday.com/blog/two-takes-depression/201407/genetic-testing-better-depression-treatment. Accessed 2/20/21.

[319] Wright, 42–43.

[320] Ibid.

[321] Ibid.

[322] Zetin, 50.

[323] Burgess, 24.

[324] "What Is Neurofeedback?" International Society for Neurofeedback & Research pamphlet. 16553-Article-Text-64896-1-10-20160826.pdf. Accessed 2/20/21.

[325] "Depression (Major Depressive Disorder)," 8.

[326] Zetin, 408.

[327] Ibid, 410.

[328] Zetin, 410.

[329] "Depression (Major Depressive Disorder)," 8.

[330] Zetin, 408, 418.

[331] Ibid, 418.

[332] Burgess, 104.

[333] Zetin, 419.

[334] Ibid, 420.

[335] Burgess, 104–105.

[336] "Depression (Major Depressive Disorder)," 8.

[337] Burgess, 46.

[338] Zetin, 236.

[339] Phillips, Michael. "Army Tests Injection for PTSD." *The Wall Street Journal.* 12 June 2017. 1. https://www.wsj.com/articles/can-a-single-injection-conquer-ptsd-the-army-wants-to-find-out-1497279572?mg=prod/accounts-wsj.     Accessed 2/18/21.

[340] Ibid.

[341] Kirsch, Irving, M.D. "Antidepressants and the Placebo Effect." *Zeitschrift fur Psychologie (Journal of Psychology)*, Hogrefe Publishing, 2014. Vol. 222, Issue 3. http://econtent.hogrefe.com/doi/abs/10.1027/2151-2604/a000176. Accessed 2/18/21. 134.

[342] Ibid.

[343] Ibid.

[344] Zetin, 50.

[345] Wright, 5.

[346] Burgess, 124.

[347] Ibid, 126.

[348] Ibid, 127–128.

[349] Burgess, 25.

[350] Rao, Murali. 1.

[351] Ibid, 1.

[352] Mitchell, Heidi. "To Treat Depression, Start with a Digital Therapist." *The Wall Street Journal.* 26 June 2017. R13. 1.

[353] Ibid.

[354] Ibid.

[355] Barron, Daniel. "The Rise of Big Data Psychiatry." *The Wall Street Journal.* 29 April 2021. https://www.wsj.com/articles/the-rise-of-big-data-psychiatry-11619704849. Accessed 5-7-21.

[356] Ibid.

[357] Ibid.

[358] Ibid.

[359] "Depression (Major Depressive Disorder)," 10.

**Chapter 15**
[360] Oaklander, Mandy. "The Anti Antidepressant." *Time.* 7 August 2017. 40.

[361] Oaklander, 41.

[362] Shulman, Robert. Phone interview by Sarah Hamaker. 1 February 2021.

[363] Solovitch, Sara. "Onetime Party Drug Hailed as Miracle for Treating Severe Depression." *The Washington Post*. 1 February 2016. https://www.washingtonpost. com/national/health-science/a-one-time-party-drug-is-helping-people-with-deep-depression/2016/02/01/d3e73862-b490-11e5-a76a-0b5145e8679a_story. html. Accessed 2/20/21. 1.

[364] Ibid.

[365] Oaklander, 43.

[366] "Scaccia, Annamarya. "Could Party Drug Ketamine Be a Treatment for Depression?" RollingStone.com. 21 June 2017. http://www.rollingstone.com/culture/features/ketamine-future-of-depression-treatment-w488998. Accessed 2/20/21.

[367] Ibid.[368] Oaklander. 44.

[369] Scaccia.

[370] McMillen, Matt. "Ketamine: The Future of Depression Treatment?" WebMd. com. 23 September 2014. http://www.webmd.com/depression/news/20140923/ketamine-depression#1. Accessed 2/18/21.

[371] McMillen.

[372] Scaccia.

[373] Ibid.

[374] Chen, Jennifer. "How New Ketamine Drug Helps with Depression." Yale Medicine.org. 21 March 2019. https://www.yalemedicine.org/news/ketamine-depression. Accessed 2/26/21.

[375] Ibid.

[376] Ibid.

[377] Torborg, Liza and Vande Voort, Jennifer, M.D. "Mayo Clinic Q and A: New Treatment for Hard-to-Treat Depression." Mayo Clinic.org. 12 July 2019. https://newsnetwork.mayoclinic.org/discussion/mayo-clinic-q-and-a-new-treatment-for-hard-to-treat-depression. Accessed 2/26/21.

[378] Ibid.

[379] Gordon, Joshua, M.D. National Institute of Mental Health. "New Hope for Treatment-Resistant Depression: Guessing Right on Ketamine." NIMH.gov. 13 August 2019. https://www.nimh.nih.gov/about/director/messages/2019/new-hope-for-treatment-resistant-depression-guessing-right-on-ketamine.shtml.

Accessed 2/26/21.

[380] Ibid.

[381] Ibid.

[382] Chen.

[383] Torborg.

[384] Gordon.

[385] "FDA Approves First Treatment for Postpartum Depression." FDA.gov. 19 March 2019. https://www.fda.gov/news-events/press-announcements/fda-approves-first-treatment-post-partum-depression. Accessed 2/26/21.

[386] Nogrady, Bianca. "Antidepressant Approvals Could Herald New Era in Psychiatric Drugs." The-Scientist.com. 1 October 2019. https://www.the-scientist.com/bio-business/antidepressant-approvals-could-herald-new-era-in-psychiatric-drugs-66475. Accessed 2/26/21.

[387] Ibid.

[388] Ibid.

[389] Azar, Adnan. "Five Ways AI Can Help Revolutionize Mental Healthcare." Forbes.com. 19 August 2020. https://www.forbes.com/sites/forbestechcouncil/2020/08/19/five-ways-ai-can-help-revolutionize-mental-healthcare/?sh=4c646ca513ab. Accessed 2/26/21.

[390] Clarke, Jodi. "Can Artificial Intelligence Help with Depression?" Very Well Mind.com. https://www.verywellmind.com/can-artificial-intelligence-help-depression-4158330. Accessed 2/27/21.

[391] Ibid.

[392] Ibid.

[393] Azar.

[394] Ibid.

[395] Ibid.

[396] "Gene Therapy for Depression: A Futuristic Treatment." *Mental Health Daily*.com. http://mentalhealthdaily.com/2015/08/21/gene-therapy-for-depression-a-futuristic-treatment. Accessed 2/16/21.

[397] Kluger, Jeffrey. "New Clues to Depression Spotted in the Genome." Time.com. 1 August 2016. http://time.com/4431292/depression-genome. Accessed 2/18/21.

[398] Ibid.

[399] Oaklander, 44.

[400] "Gene Therapy for Depression: A Futuristic Treatment."

[401] "Genetic Variation Linked to Response to Anxiety Could Inform Personalized Therapies." Science Daily.com. 2 July 2019. https://www.sciencedaily.com/releases/2019/07/190702112813.htm. Accessed 2/18/21.

[402] Ibid.

[403] Sandoiu, Ana. "Depression: Gene-Activating Drug Reverses Symptoms in Mice." *Medical News Today.* 19 February 2019. https://www.medicalnewstoday.com/articles/324492. Accessed 2/18/21.

[404] Ibid.

[405] Morris, Nathaniel. "Take a Pill to Ward Off Depression?" *The Washington Post.* 19 September 2017. E5.

[406] Ibid.

[407] Ibid.

[408] Ibid.

[409] Ibid.

[410] Ibid.

[411] Ibid.

[412] Ibid.

[413] Ibid.

[414] Ibid.

[415] Schmidt, Charles. "Mental Health May Depend on Creatures in the Gut." Scientific American. 1 March 2015. https://www.scientificamerican.com/article/mental-health-may-depend-on-creatures-in-the-gut/?print=true. Accessed 2/20/21.

[416] Sanders, Laura. "Microbes Can Play Games with the Mind." Science News.org. 23 March 2016. https://www.sciencenews.org/article/microbes-can-play-games-mind. Accessed 2/20/21.

[417] Ibid.

[418] Schmidt.

[419] Ibid.

[420] Hendriksen, Ellen, Ph.D. "Is Your Gut Making You Depressed or Anxious?" QuickandDirtyTips.com. 6 April 2018. http://www.quickanddirtytips.com/health-fitness/mental-health/is-your-gut-making-you-depressed-or-anxious?utm_source=sciam&utm_campaign=sciam. Accessed 2/18/21.

[421] Sanders.

[422] Svoboda, Elizabeth. "Gut Bacteria's Role in Anxiety and Depression: It's Not Just in Your Head." *Discover Magazine*. 4 October 2020. https://www.discovermagazine.com/mind/gut-bacterias-role-in-anxiety-and-depression-its-not-just-in-your-head. Accessed 2/27/21.

[423] Ibid.

[424] Ibid.

[425] Ibid.

[426] Ibid.

[427] Ibid.

[428] Ibid.

[429] Ibid.

[430] Ibid.

[431] Hall-Flavin, Daniel K. "Natural Remedies for Depression: Are They Effective?" MayoClinic.org. http://www.mayoclinic.org/diseases-conditions/depression/expert-answers/natural-remedies-for-depression/faq-20058026. Accessed 2/18/21.

[432] Norman, Suzanne. Phone interview by Sarah Hamaker. 15 September 2017.

[433] Ibid.

[434] Ibid.

[435] Grohol, John M., Psy.D. "Alternative Treatments for Depression." PsychCentral.com.

[436] Ibid.

[437] Hall-Flavin.

[438] Ibid.

[439] Ibid.

[440] Hall-Flavin.

[441] Ibid.

[442] Ibid.

## Chapter 16

[443] Hurley, Dan. "The Return of Electroshock Therapy." *The Atlantic*. December 2015. http://www.theatlantic.com/magazine/archive/2015/12/the-return-of-electroshock-therapy/413179. Accessed 2/18/21. 1.

[444] Dukakis, Kitty, and Larry Tye. *Shock: The Healing Power of Electroconvulsive Therapy*. London: Penguin Group (USA), Inc., 2006. 1.

[445] Ibid. 10.

[446] Burgess, 105.

[447] "Electroconvulsive Therapy (ECT)." MayoClinic.org. 25 October 2012. http://www.mayoclinic.org/tests-procedures/electroconvulsive-therapy/basics/definition/PRC-20014161. Accessed 2/16/21. 2.

[448] Burgess, 105.

[449] Groberman, Alex. "Shock Treatments for Depression." PsyWeb.com. 23 May 2012. 1.

[450] Engel, 71.

[451] Groberman, 1.

[452] "Electroconvulsive Therapy (ECT)." 1.

[453] Engel, 240–241.

[454] Fink, M. "What Was Learned: Studies by the Consortium for Research in ECT (CORE) 1997–2011." U.S. National Library of Medicine National Institutes of Health. 12 February 2014. http://www.ncbi.nlm.nih.gov/pubmed/24571807. 129(6), pp. 417-26. 12 Accessed 2/16/21.

[455] "Electroconvulsive Therapy (ECT)." 1.

[456] Ibid, 6.

[457] Ibid, 5.

[458] Ibid.

[459] Dukakis, 4.

[460] Burgess, 105.

[461] "Electroconvulsive Therapy (ECT)." 6.

[462] Dukakis, 5.

[463] Ibid, 10.

## Chapter 17

[464] Marchand, William R., M.D. *Depression and Bipolar Disorder: Your Guide to Recovery*. Boulder, Colorado: Bull Publishing Company, 2012. 202.

[465] Senner, Bonnie. Phone interview by Sarah Hamaker. Tape recording. 5 August 2015.

[466] Greenlaw, Ellen. "Getting Started: Talk Therapy for Depression." WebMD.com.

6 July 2010. http://www.webmd.com/depression/features/therapy-therapist. Accessed 11/13/15. 1.

[467] Ibid, 2.

[468] Phelps, Jim, M.D. *Why Am I Still Depressed?: Recognizing and Managing the Ups and Downs of Bipolar II and Soft Bipolar Disorder*. New York, N.Y.: McGraw-Hill, 2006. 231.

[469] Ibid, 229.

[470] Marchand, 204.

[471] Phelps, 229.

[472] DeRubeis, Robert J., Greg J. Siegle, and Steven D. Hollon. "Cognitive Therapy versus Medications for Depression: Treatment Outcomes and Neural Mechanisms." Nature Reviews Neuroscience. Nature.com. October 2008. 788–796. https://doi.org/10.1038/nrn2345. Accessed 2/10/21. 788.

[473] Wehrenberg, Margaret. *The 10 Best-Ever Depression Management Techniques: Understanding How Your Brain Makes You Depressed & What You Can Do to Change It*. New York, N.Y.: W.W. Norton & Company, 2010. 7.

[474] Marchand, 204.

[475] Ibid, 205.

[476] Shedler, Jonathan. "The Efficacy of Psychodynamic Psychotherapy." *American Psychologist*. February–March 2010. http://www.apa.org/pubs/journals/releases/amp-65-2-98.pdf. Accessed 2/20/21.

[477] Phelps, 231.

[478] Marchand, 213.

[479] Ilardi, Stephen S., Ph.D. *The Depression Cure: The 6-Step Program to Beat Depression without Drugs*. Cambridge, Mass.: Da Capo Press, 2009. 191.

[480] Ibid, 188.

[481] Ibid, 174.

[482] Itkowitz, Colby. "Finding Hope on a Park Bench." *The Washington Post*. 18 July 2017. E1.

[483] Ibid.

[484] Marchand, 216.

[485] Wehrenberg, 5–6.

[486] Greenlaw, 3.

## Chapter 18

[487] Serpell, James. "Animal Companions and Human Well-Being: An Historical Exploration of the Value of Human-Animal Relationships." *Handbook on Animal-Assisted Therapy: Theoretical Foundations and Guidelines for Practice*. Cambridge, Massachusetts: Academic Press, 2000. 3–17.

[488] Cozzolino, Callandre. Phone interview by Sarah Hamaker. Tape recording. 25 August 2015.

[489] Landau, Elizabeth. "Dogs First Domesticated in Europe, Study Says." CNN Health. 14 November 2013. http://www.cnn.com/2013/11/14/health/dogs-domesticated-europe. Accessed 2/18/21.

[490] "Service Animals and Assisted-Animal Therapy." reSearch. Volume 8, Issue 1. National Rehabilitation Information Center. http://www.naric.com/?q=en/publications/volume-8-issue-1-service-animals-and-assisted-animal-therapy. Accessed 2/20/21.

[491] Ilardi, 186–187.

[492] Marchand, 229.

[493] Phelps, 228.

[494] Doheny, Kathleen. "Pets for Depression and Health: Can Your Depression Problems Improve When You Interact with Your Pet?" WebMD.com 3 August 2012. http://www.webmd.com/depression/features/pets-depression. Accessed 11/13/15. 2.

## Chapter 19

[495] Marchand, 218.

[496] Rivera, Zak. Phone interview by Sarah Hamaker. Tape recording. 28 August 2015.

[497] Ilardi, 132.

[498] Ibid, 15.

[499] Ibid, 117.

[500] Wehrenberg, 130.

[501] Ilardi, 120.

[502] Marchand, 219.

[503] Wehrenberg, 130.

[504] Ilardi, 119.

505 Ilardi, 243.

506 Wehrenberg, 122; Ilardi, 131.

507 Wehrenberg, 131.

508 Ibid, 134.

509 Weintraub, Amy. *Yoga for Depression: A Compassionate Guide to Relieve Suffering through Yoga*. New York, New York: Broadway Books, 2004. 131.

510 Ibid, 9.

511 Ibid.

512 Ibid.

513 Ibid.

514 Ibid.

515 Ibid, 10.

516 Stratton, Andrew. "Personal Trainer—History of This Practice." EzineArticles. com. 30 April 2010. http://ezinearticles.com/?Personal-Trainer---History-of-This-Practice&id=4206058. Accessed 2/22/21.

**Chapter 20**

517 Wright, 269.

518 Burgess, 150.

519 Rao, 1.

520 Ilardi, 67.

521 Ibid, 74.

522 Rao, 4.

523 Emmons, Henry, MD. *The Chemistry of Joy: A Three-Step Program for Overcoming Depression through Western Science and Eastern Wisdom*. New York, New York: Simon & Schuster, 2006. 78–79.

524 Ibid, 77-78.

525 Rao, 1.

526 Burgess, 155.

527 Ibid.

528 Wright, 270.

529 Ibid.

530 Burgess, 155.

531 Wright, 270.

[532] Burgess, 151.

[533] Wright, 26.

[534] Rao, 5.

[535] Emmons, 73.

[536] Rao, 5.

[537] Emmons, 74.

[538] Ibid, 76.

[539] Ilardi, 6.

[540] Burgess, 152.

[541] Wright, 26.

[542] Rao, 3.

[543] Ibid.

[544] Emmons, 77.

[545] Rao, 6.

[546] Wright, 270.

[547] Emmons, 72.

[548] Burgess, 150.

[549] Emmons, 76.

## Chapter 23

[550] "Depression Recovery: An Overview." WebMD.com. 27 September 2020. http://www.webmd.com/depression/recovery-overview. Accessed 2/10/21. 1.

[551] Ibid.

[552] Ibid.

[553] "Recovery and Staying Well." Beyondblue.org. https://www.beyondblue.org.au/get-support/recovery-and-staying-well. Accessed 12/3/15.

## Chapter 24

[554] "Family and Friends' Guide to Recovery from Depression and Bipolar Disorder." Depression and Bipolar Support Alliance. 2006.

## Conclusion

[555] Holmes, Lindsay. "11 Statistics that Will Change the Way You Think About Depression." *The Huffington Post*. 21 January 2015. http://www.huffingtonpost.

com/2015/01/20/depression-statistics_n_6480412.html. Accessed 2/18/21. 1.

[556] Ibid.

[557] "Depression Facts." U.S. Centers for Disease Control and Prevention website. http://www.cdc.gov/nchs/fastats/depression.htm. Accessed 12/3/15. 1.

[558] Holmes, 1.

[559] Ibid.

# ABOUT THE AUTHOR

A graduate of Texas Christian University, Mark Litzsinger is the former chairman of Follett Corporation. Now retired, he spends time sailing and traveling. Mark shows his Samoyeds (Sanibel, Aston, and Benz), as well as his collection of antique cars, including a 1935 Packard Twelve 1207 Coupe Roadster. In addition, he's an entrepreneur, inventor and mentor. Mark also gives talks about his experiences with depression. He is a firm believer in giving back to society. *Climbing Toward the Light* is the third edition of his first book.

Made in the USA
Monee, IL
30 March 2024

55441245R00154